To Finley J,
Christmas 2015.

With love

Uncle Andrew x

KU-281-527

STAR WARS™

COMPLETE VEHICLES

STAR WARS™

COMPLETE VEHICLES

Written by
Kerrie Dougherty
Curtis Saxton
David West Reynolds
Ryder Windham

Illustrated by
Hans Jenssen and Richard Chasemore

Additional illustrations by
John Mullaney, Jon Hall

www.dk.com

CONTENTS

FOREWORD

Ever since childhood, I've been a fan of cool hardware design. In the late 1960s, my father built a model kit of a nuclear submarine called the *USS Patrick Henry*. This model was cut-away on one side and included a detailed interior. I studied that model intently, trying to understand why everything was where it was and how the space was used. This fascination continued when I later came across sectional drawings of World War II aircraft carriers and battleships. I would marvel at their complexity, but I could see the logic of the design—form followed from function.

As I became interested in film, and science fiction films in particular, I also became fascinated by the internal workings of the hardware seen in these movies. I wanted to know how these futuristic spaceships were meant to work, and I appreciated it when it was clear that the movie designers had put some serious thought into the design of the vehicles. I spent many hours looking through *The Making of 2001–A Space Odyssey*, trying to piece together how all of the interior movie sets of the starship *Discovery* would fit together inside the fictional vessel's spherical hull.

And then came *Star Wars*. Here was a picture where everyone involved clearly cared about making the *Star Wars* universe look functional, believable, and real. Everything had an authentic look, one that was lived-in and used. It made sense to me when I later discovered that Ralph McQuarrie had worked for Boeing, and that Joe Johnston, John Dykstra, Grant McCune, and many of the first crew at Industrial Light & Magic (ILM) had industrial design backgrounds. Twenty years later, I found myself working at ILM and participating in the *Star Wars* prequel trilogy. I now had the distinct pleasure of watching the design process from the inside. I got to see George Lucas's ideas go from written description to simple sketches, then to refined drawings, and finally to highly detailed miniatures or computer graphics.

Working very closely with the artists during all of this, I saw (and participated in) a number of little cheats to get through the required action with the approved designs. These were little things, like the fact that the landing gears for the Queen's Royal Starship were too tall to fold up into the underside of the craft, or that R2-D2's "shoulders" couldn't have fitted into a Naboo starfighter without making unsightly bulges in the hull.

Consequently, I really admire the thought, planning, and meticulous detail that Hans Jenssen and Richard Chasemore put into the drawings in this book. In many cases, with the help of the writers, they've resolved our design cheats—I especially like what they did with R2-D2's shoulders in the Naboo starfighter! They've taken the process that the concept designers started and painstakingly brought it to conclusion, filling in the millions of details we never had time to think about. In that sense, *Complete Vehicles* is the last chapter in the creation of the vehicles of the *Star Wars* saga.

JOHN KNOLL
VISUAL EFFECTS SUPERVISOR, ILM
EPISODES I–III

THE OLD REPUBLIC

Over 25,000 years ago, the introduction of hyperdrive technology made it possible for settlers to spread throughout the galaxy. After much exploration and colonization, a significant proportion of inhabited star systems united to form a democratic Galactic Republic. During this era, artistic expression and functional practicality drove vehicle design. Centuries of complacency and corruption, however, have led to political turmoil. New and unusual technologies and designs emerge as the Separatist movement entices many star systems to break away from the Republic. Greedy commercial organizations, aligned with the Separatist cause, create craft with dual military/commercial uses, often incorporating droid technologies, while the Republic responds with new military vehicles to aid the Jedi in their attempts to maintain peace and stability.

NABOO DESIGN

The sleek and elegant lines of the Naboo N-1 starfighter exemplify the ancient traditions of artistic craftsmanship—the hallmark of starship design in the Republic era. However, the N-1's aesthetic appeal does not supersede its practical capabilities, and the vehicle is well-suited to its role in the planet's Security Forces. When necessary, it can become a fearsome adversary in combat.

DROID TECHNOLOGY

The droid tri-fighter symbolizes the demise of the Republic's traditions of artistic design. The droid vehicles and weaponry utilized by the Separatists are functional, expendable, cheaply mass-produced, and unaffected by human concerns for self-preservation. Craft design is often based on the appearance of terrifying alien predators and represents the triumph of ruthless pragmatism over artistic expression.

DEFENDERS OF THE REPUBLIC

For millennia, Jedi Knights have maintained peace and security throughout the galaxy, using the Republic's diplomatic vessels for transport and assistance with "aggressive negotiations." However, as the threat from the Separatist movement progresses into the galaxy-wide conflict known as the Clone Wars, the Jedi require new starfighters to defend the Republic. The fast, agile Jedi Interceptor combines elegant yet practical design with lethal effectiveness and has become a symbol of authority and hope for the Republic's forces.

COMMERCIAL FORCES

The Trade Federation is a leading power amongst the merchant factions seeking the overthrow of the Republic. The organization combines its commercial and military aims by making dual use of many of its craft, such as converting cargo vessels into Droid Control Ships to transport and coordinate its droid armies. Foreshadowing the Empire's mass-production of spacecraft, the Trade Federation and its allies use modified versions of a small selection of vehicles for a wide range of uses, thereby achieving maximum effectiveness at minimal cost.

THE GALACTIC EMPIRE

The Republic's transformation into the Galactic Empire ends the chaos of the Clone Wars, but heralds an oppressive new era in which the citizens are subjugated under a terrifying dictatorship. To help the Empire maintain its iron grip, the regime develops many new weapon technologies. The Rebel Alliance—a small army of united dissidents fighting against Imperial rule—poses a threat to the New Order. To restrict the rebels' access to Imperial technologies, many manufacturers are brought under Imperial control or shut down, while other organizations become dominant due to lucrative Imperial contracts. Consequently, the variety of craft and vehicle designs produced is greatly reduced compared to the days of the Old Republic, as mass-production replaces traditional craftsmanship.

IMPERIAL ENFORCER

The heavily armed TIE (Twin Ion Engine) bomber is an important component of the Empire's enforcement arsenal, used to blast rebellious communities into submission, or to destroy spacecraft in flight. It is a good example of the Imperial practice of adapting a small selection of basic designs and using them for various purposes. The versatile TIE fighter-craft design is readily adaptable and has become a "workhorse" vehicle for the Galactic Empire.

REIGN OF TERROR

Imperial Star Destroyers—massive capital ships with enormous firepower—are used to maintain control across the Empire. The first Star Destroyers were developed by the Republic during the Clone Wars. The emergent Empire refined and developed the Star Destroyer design, augmenting its firepower and capacity to carry assault forces. The result was an instrument of terror built to crush all opposition to Imperial rule.

ASSAULT BEHEMOTH

In addition to its relentless space- and aerial-attack forces, the Empire deploys heavy ground-assault vehicles to crush its enemies into submission. The giant AT-AT (All Terrain Armored Transport) walkers are utilized across the galaxy as troop transports and attack craft. Their size and firepower exemplify Emperor Palpatine's objective of total subjugation through the use of awe-inspiring military might.

THE REBEL RESPONSE

In the face of overwhelming Imperial forces, the Rebel Alliance retaliates with an assortment of craft and weapons. Disaffected engineers and designers, who do not want to work under Imperial rule, join the Alliance and form the backbone of its military design capabilities. Despite limited access to components and manufacturing facilities, the Alliance designs and builds fast, well-armed, and maneuverable ships— including the T-65 X-wing—to battle against Imperial oppression.

TECHNOLOGY

The technology in use throughout the galaxy during both the era of the Old Republic and the reign of the Galactic Empire is the long-established product of millennia of scientific and technical research on many worlds. For 25,000 years, hyperdrive technology has made space travel safe and routine. There are few completely new innovations, but myriad variations on the basic technological principles can be found galaxy-wide. Sophisticated devices incorporating computing technologies are integral to the operation of galactic society, as well as its vehicles and equipment. Mechatronics technologies have provided a cheap and expendable labor force—droids, which can be designed to perform virtually any task. In the upheaval created by the downfall of the Old Republic, the rise of the Empire, and the ensuing Galactic Civil War, military technologies come to the fore, as opposing parties create weapons and warcraft that will provide tactical and strategic advantage.

HYPERSPACE COMMUNICATIONS

Supralight hyperwaves, traveling through hyperspace, enable signals to be carried instantaneously across the galaxy. The public HoloNet uses hyperwaves to allow real-time communication between planets and starships. Military, rebel, and pirate groups use their own secure hyperwave communication systems.

Communications antenna

Sensor computer

Primary sensor array

Repulsorlift

Proton torpedo

SENSOR SYSTEMS

Sensors analyze the environment around a vehicle for threats and hazards. Scanners and other instruments survey the surrounding area at different ranges, feeding back information that is processed by the sensor computer.

GRAVITY TECHNOLOGIES

Modern galactic civilization uses a variety of devices to manipulate gravity. Repulsorlift technology allows a craft to hover or fly over a planetary surface, and inertial compensators enable spacecraft crews to carry out high-speed maneuvers without being pulverized by gravitational forces. Tractor beams manipulate gravitational forces to move or retrieve objects. All these devices use subnuclear "knots" of space-time to control gravity. These knots are the products of massive, automated power-refineries that surround black holes and process their space-time fields.

HYPERDRIVE AND SUBLIGHT ENGINES

A hyperdrive-equipped starship can accomplish faster-than-light travel, via the eerie realm of hyperspace. Hyperdrives utilize supralight "hypermatter" particles to allow a jump to lightspeed without changing the complex mass/energy configuration of the ship. The hyperdrive field, once generated, must be projected around the starship to enable it to remain in hyperspace—a drive system failure will result in the ship dropping out of hyperspace back into real space in a potentially dangerous location, such as an asteroid belt. Sublight engines propel spacecraft in real space. They are used for orbital operations, during space battles, and when traveling within planetary systems. The most common type of sublight engine is the ion drive, which produces thrust by projecting a stream of charged particles through the engine's exhaust port. Fuels can include pressurized radioactive gas, volatile composite mixtures, and explosive liquid metals.

POWER SOURCES

Starships and vehicles use a hierarchy of power technologies that were perfected in pre-Republic times. Domestic devices generally run on portable chemical, fission, and fusion reactors. These systems consume a variety of fuels, depending upon local resources. Most starships use fusion systems that contain more powerful hypermatter-annihilation cores.

Astromech droid

Power generator

Laser cannon

ASTROMECH DROIDS

Specifically designed to work with spacecraft, astromech droids can operate both as an independent unit and as an integral part of the ship. They can function equally well inside the vessel or in the vacuum of space. As ship-units, astromechs interface with their craft's computer systems to augment the capabilities of ship and pilot. They monitor and diagnose flight performance, calculate and store hyperspace data, and pinpoint technical errors or faulty computer-coding. As independent units, most astromechs are programmed to repair a variety of different vehicles and are used as on-board and ground-based repair and maintenance crews.

Sublight engine

Hyperdrive

Deflector shield projectors

SHIELDS

Ships and vehicles are protected by force fields that repel solid objects or absorb energy. Constant power is required to dissipate the energy from impacts. Concussion shields repel space debris, and deflector shields (ray and particle shields) help protect craft during battle. Ray shields deflect or break up the beams from energy weapons. Particle shields protect against impact from projectiles and proton weapons. Shield intensities diminish with distance from the generator or projector, although shields projected in an atmosphere tend to have a defined outer surface. When a shield absorbs large energy blasts, the momentum can surge back to the ship or vehicle, affecting its motion.

ARMAMENT

Laser cannons and turbolasers fire invisible energy beams that travel at lightspeed. A glowing pulse traveling along the beam at less than lightspeed marks the energy bolt's path. However, the light given off by this visible pulse depletes the overall energy content of the beam. Blasters and ion cannons are also classed as energy weapons—blasters fire powerful bolts created by the excitation of high-energy gas while ion cannons emit bursts of ionized energy. Proton weapons are physical ordnance, which cause destruction by releasing clouds of high-energy, high-velocity proton particles. Proton torpedoes are among the most powerful weapons carried by starfighters, but they are secondary to laser cannons, as only a limited number of torpedoes can be carried.

EPISODE I
THE PHANTOM MENACE

The Galactic Republic is engulfed by turmoil. Thousands of years of peace and prosperity are threatened by the greed of powerful new commercial organizations, such as the Trade Federation, which have risen to challenge the authority of the Galactic Senate. To resolve disputes, the Republic must call on the negotiating skills of its guardians of peace and justice, the Jedi Knights. During their efforts to resolve one such flash point—the blockade of the planet Naboo by the Trade Federation—Jedi Master Qui-Gon Jinn and his Padawan, Obi-Wan Kenobi, become embroiled in a complex plot that ultimately leads them to the desert planet Tatooine. There they discover a young slave, Anakin Skywalker, who shows amazing Force-potential. Qui-Gon believes he may be the "Chosen One" of Jedi lore, destined to bring balance to the Force.

REPUBLIC CRUISER

Carrying two Jedi Knights into the heart of danger, the Republic cruiser is dispatched by Supreme Chancellor Valorum to the blockaded planet of Naboo. The direct predecessor to the well-armed Blockade Runner corvette, the peaceful Republic cruiser was assembled in the great orbital shipyards of Corellia, and serves as a testament to the quality and fame of Corellian spacecraft design. The *Radiant VII* is a veteran of 34 years in service of the diplomatic corps of Coruscant itself, capital world of the Galactic Republic. The ship has endured many adventures, bringing Jedi Knights, ambassadors, and diplomats to trouble spots around the galaxy on missions of security and vital political significance. Its interchangeable salon pods are well-armored and insulated against any kind of eavesdropping. In this safe haven, critical negotiations can take place and crises can be averted.

Dyne 577
sublight engine

Deflector shield
energizer

Deflector
shield
generator

Radiator panel wing

Cooling
shroud

Magnetic
turbine

Deflector shield
projector

Standard space
docking ring

Primary power cell

Secondary
power cell

Charged fuel line

Fuel driver

Fuel atomizer cone

Igniters

Radiation
dampers

Ion generator ring ionizes ignited
fuel prior to turbine injection

Droid hold

8-person
escape pod

COLOR SIGNAL

The striking red color of the Republic cruiser sends a message to all who see it. Scarlet declares the ship's diplomatic immunity and serves as a warning not to attack. Red is the color of ambassadorial relations and neutrality for spacecraft of the Galactic Republic, and has been for generations. The tradition will continue even into the days of the Empire: Princess Leia Organa's consular vessel *Tantive IV* of Alderaan is striped in red to indicate its special diplomatic status. The extraordinary full-red color scheme of the Republic cruiser signifies that the ship comes straight from the great capital world of the Republic, Coruscant.

Control Console The Republic cruiser's control console is engineered to allow the captain and co-pilot to share operational duties, or if necessary for just one of them to pilot the ship.

Mission to Naboo Approaching heavily armed Trade Federation cargo ships in orbit around Naboo, the *Radiant VII* maintains full shield power until it lands in a cargo ship's hangar.

COMMUNICATING IN A DIVERSE GALAXY

In order to communicate with any culture it may visit, the Republic cruiser sports a wide variety of dish and other communications antennae. On board the cruiser, two communications officers specialize in operating the communication computers, deciphering strange languages, and decoding the complex signal pulses of unorthodox alien transmissions. Years later, the Empire will standardize communications across the galaxy, making such systems unnecessary.

Upper deck state rooms

Wiring and systems trunk

Formal dining room

Crew lounge

Elevator

Multi-comm station

Salon pod magnoclamps

Navigator's station

Captain's storage

Automated docking signal receiver

Cockpit

Navigational sensor dish

Lounge

Escape pod access tunnel (from lower deck)

Captain's quarters

Salon vestibule

Salon pod breakaway cowling

Interchangeable diplomatic salon pod

Main salon pod airlock doors

Salon pod has seating for 16 beings

Hologram pad

Main forward sensors

Salon pod independent sensors

Mid-deck corridor

TIGHT SECURITY

The *Radiant VII* is a modified Corellian cruiser. Civilian models of the class are used for straightforward transport purposes, but the scarlet Republic cruisers are dedicated to the special objectives of galactic political service. To accomplish their missions, Republic cruisers must often rely on their reputation as absolutely secure vessels for high-level diplomatic meetings and confrontations. For security reasons, crew is kept to a bare minimum, with many ship functions attended by simple utility droids.

DANGEROUS DIPLOMACY

Although the planet Naboo is a member world of the Galactic Republic, it is located near the Outer Rim Territories, where the Republic has little influence. There, worlds without strong military forces are especially vulnerable to attack and invasion. Because the Neimoidian homeworld is also a member of the Republic, and because the Neimoidians rarely take any action that invites trouble with the Republic, the Neimoidian Trade Federation's blockade of Naboo surprises many representatives of the Galactic Senate. When a Republic cruiser delivers a Jedi Knight and his apprentice to a Trade Federation battleship in Naboo's orbit, the Jedi know that if they fail to persuade the Neimoidians to leave the Naboo system, violent conflict could result.

Cruiser Cockpit After successfully delivering the Jedi Knights Qui-Gon Jinn and Obi-Wan Kenobi to a Trade Federation ship, co-pilot Antidar Williams and Captain Maoi Madakor watch helplessly as a droid laser turret targets the *Radiant VII*'s cockpit.

Treacherous Hosts Docked within a Trade Federation cargo ship that has been upgraded with military-grade weapons, the *Radiant VII* becomes vulnerable to attack when the crew lowers its deflector shields.

REPUBLIC CRUISER SALON POD

Republic cruisers often serve as neutral meeting grounds for Republic officials and leaders of groups in conflict. To accommodate the many kinds of alien physiology in the galaxy, customized salon pods are available in the hangars on Coruscant, and the Republic cruiser can be equipped with any of these. In emergency situations, the entire salon pod can eject from the cruiser with its own sensors and independent life-support gear ready to sustain the diplomatic party on board. Unfortunately for the crew of the *Radiant VII*, when their ship is attacked there is no time for such an escape.

Hull breach adjacent to navigator's station

Severe battle damage

Magnoclamps are disengaged

Independent pod sensors activate

Breakaway cowling releases

Salon pod thrusters fire

DROID INVASION FORCES

The Neimoidian Trade Federation uses a standard plan to invade worlds they hope to dominate. First, an armada of battleships surrounds the targeted world. The battleships deploy Xi Char-manufactured droid starfighters to disable any satellite weapons and communications systems, and send C-9979 landing ships to the world's surface. Each landing ship carries Trade Federation battle droids, tanks, and transports. An orbital Droid Control Ship directs the droids to attack, capture, or destroy the enemy's strategic defenses. Every battle droid obeys orders with ruthless efficiency.

Deployed Landing Ships Each retrofitted Trade Federation cargo ship carries 50 landing ships for transporting war machines and droids to planetary surfaces. Externally, they resemble the Trade Federation's standard commercial cargo barges.

Droid Army Disembarks Operated by the Trade Federation's remote Droid Control Ship, battle droids guide Multi-Troop Transports (MTTs) out of the landing ships and steer them into strategic positions.

Drive unit adapted from civilian cargo sled

Repulsorlift sled

TROOP CARRIER

The Trade Federation troop carrier conveys battle droid units to deployment zones behind the protection of ground armor, in secure conditions, or within occupied areas. A rack similar to that in the MTT contains a full complement of 112 battle droids folded into their space-saving configuration, ready for action on release.

The Conquest of Naboo The droid army descends on the capital city of Naboo, Theed. The force is so overwhelming that no resistance is offered, and the city falls without a battle.

LANDING SHIP

When plans for the ground forces of the Trade Federation secret army had begun to take shape, methods of deployment came under consideration. The Haor Chall Engineering works produced a design for a landing craft that would carry attack vehicles and troops to ground sites from Trade Federation battleships, and, after a period of much-debated development, the C-9979 variant was chosen by the Trade Federation armaments committee. Related in design to commercial cargo barges in the trade fleet, these huge, double-winged ships were built for the sole purpose of transporting AATs (Armored Assault Tanks), troop carriers, and MTTs (Multi-Troop Transports) from orbiting battleships to strategic positions on planet surfaces. The C-9979 offers tremendous antigravity lifting capacity, which is necessary for the heavy, armored cargo. With its defensive laser cannons, the mighty C-9979 presents a bizarre and menacing shadow in the skies of any threatened planet.

MECHANIZED CREW

A relatively small droid crew operates the C-9979, in keeping with the Trade Federation reliance on completely automated soldiery. Droid pilots steer the ship and robot gunners work the cannon stations, which serve to defend the landing ship on its way down. Along the front of the wings are a series of maintenance and repair shops. These are also run by droids, and are used to service and maintain the attack-force components, especially individual battle droids, which need realignment and repair after battle engagements.

Aft-wing tensor field generator

Aft-wing

Radiant ion drive engines

MTT being guided down ramp for deployment

Deployment ramp

AAT garages

Battle droid troop carrier column

AAT columns

Power coupling

Power cells

Structural beam energized by fore-wing tensor field

Antigravity stabilizer node

Droid maintenance and repair shops

Wing-tip blaster cannons

Fore wing

LOADING

C-9979 landing ships are berthed in hidden hangar areas aboard Trade Federation battleships. Here they are assembled, serviced, and maintained, and when ready for deployment they are loaded with MTTs, AATs, and troop carriers that have been prepared for combat. Landing ships are stored in an unloaded condition, both to reduce structural stress and enable the attack craft to be serviced individually.

Invaders Descend
The C-9979 aims for terrain that allows clearance for the ship's broad wings, but the landing gear has a relatively small footprint for such a large vessel.

Electromagnetic transport clamp-on rail will guide MTT down deployment ramp

Pressure charging turbine atmosphere intake

Control center

Control signal receiver picks up vital signal from the Droid Control Ship

MTT powers up its onboard repulsors in staging area

Deflector shield projectors

Cannon charging turret

Defensive laser cannon

Wing-tip plating is an alloy composite transparent to repulsor effect

Staging area

Fore-wing tensor field generator

Radiator panel for tensor power system

Navigation sensors

Combat sensors

Forward tensor field generator increases load-bearing ability of wing mounts

MTT garage

Antigravity rails support MTTs

Center MTT has deployed and an AAT now follows into position

Doors require clear landing area for opening clearance

Main deployment doors include perimeter field sensors to detect possible land mines, electrical fields, and other hazards

DEPLOYMENT

The wings of the landing ship contain rows of MTTs, AATs, and battle droid troop carriers racked in garage channels for maximum loading capacity. For deployment, the attack vehicles are guided along repulsor tracks to a staging platform. MTTs in particular require the assistance of the repulsors built into these tracks, because their onboard maneuvering equipment is not precise enough to negotiate the cramped confines of the garage zones without risking collisions. At a staging platform, the vehicles are rotated into position and seized by transport clamps, which draw them aft and guide them down the drop ramp in the landing ship's "foot." The great clamshell doors of the "foot" then open wide to release the ground forces. Deployment of the full load of vehicles on board a C-9979 can take up to 45 minutes.

STORING THE TRANSPORT

C-9979s are built with removable wings so they can be stored efficiently. Powerful tensor fields bind the wings to the fuselage when the ship is assembled for use. The huge wings of the C-9979 would tax the load-bearing capabilities of even the strongest metal alloys, making tensor fields vital for the integrity of the ship. Forward-mounted tensor fields bind the wing mounts firmly to the fuselage, while wing-mounted tensor fields keep the span of the wings from sagging.

AAT in escort position

MTT moving out for battle position

MTT

The Trade Federation's Baktoid Armor Workshop has long designed armaments for Trade Federation customers. When called upon to design and build vehicles for the Trade Federation droid army, it easily turned its resources to the creation of deadly weapons made to ensure a long line of future customers. The Trade Federation MTT (Multi-Troop Transport) was designed to convey platoons of ground troops to the battlefield and support them there. Its deployment on Naboo is its first use in a major military action; many transports had seen only training exercises on remote worlds before being used there. MTTs are designed for deployment in traditional battle lines, hence their heavy frontal armor. Reinforced and studded with case-hardened metal alloy studs, the MTT's face is designed to ram through walls so that troops may be deployed directly into enemy buildings (or "future customer buildings," as the Trade Federation often prefers to say). When ready to deploy, it opens its large front hatch to release the battle droid contingents from its huge storage rack, extended on a powerful hydraulic rail. Two droid pilots direct it according to instructions transmitted from the orbiting Droid Control Ship.

Smashing Power The dense forests of Naboo do little to impede the destructive movement of armored MTTs, which are capable of ramming through fortified structures.

Control room
escape hatch
(at rear)

Lift

Overseer catwalk

Rack operator droid

Deployment rack
extensor drive

Rack drive heat
exhaust vents

Rack
extensor
drive engine

Pressure
equalizer
valves

HEAVY LIFTING

The MTT's engine works hard to power repulsorlifts that carry a very heavy load of troops and solid armor. The repulsorlift generator's exhaust and cooling system is vented straight down toward the ground through several large vents under the vehicle. This creates a billowing storm of wind around the MTT, which lends it a powerful and menacing air.

Power converter
grids

Kuat Premion Mk. II
power generators

Repulsor motor gas cooling
system exhaust

Heavy-duty repulsor
cooling fins

Control signal receiver

Control room

Battle droid pilot

Battle droid engineer/ gunner

THE BAKTOID SIGNATURE IN DESIGN

The MTT was designed by the same Baktoid workshop that developed the AAT (Armored Assault Tank) for the Trade Federation secret army. The distinctive Baktoid style gives both vehicles a look reminiscent of heavy, jungle-dwelling animals. Both are designed for use in formal battle lines and place vital equipment such as reactor and main engines at the rear, protected behind the heavy armor of the front surfaces.

Droid guns stored on backpacks

Droid soldiers racked in compressed form for maximum capacity

Main troop deployment hatch

Troop deployment rack extends to release droid soldiers

THE DEPLOYMENT RACK

The original design of the MTT called for an open staging chamber inside it, but the Baktoid Armor Workshop is known for its original designs, and the MTT had the unusual job of conveying soldiers that were not living beings, but droids. The Baktoid engineers worked out a system that would load battle droids folded into very small configurations into a giant deployment rack. This rack would more than double the troop capacity of the MTT, extending to release the compressed troops which would then unfold into fighting configuration. At the conclusion of a battle, troops are reloaded into the rack and safely carried back to their base. The original, open-staging chamber MTT design was retained for carrying wheel-like destroyer droids.

Battle droids unfold to combat stance when deployed

Twin blaster cannons in ball turrets

Laser power capacitor

Laser power modulator

Heavy forward armor

Lower troop deployment hatch

PROPULSION

The sub uses rotating fins to cycle water through an electromotive field that actually drives the ship. The fins contain flat, flexible electronic units linked in series, which send electrical impulses down their length, pushing the water along. Combined with the rotating fins, this electromotive field can grab onto and displace a great deal of water, hurtling the sub through the sea at great speed. The power unit just inside the rear of the sub provides primary power for the electromotive field and the cockpit field generators. The sub's repulsorlift discs (on the underside) are typically used only for launch and docking, when the electromotive field is not in use.

Electromotive impulse field carriers

Flexible electromotive fins drive and steer the sub

Secondary drive fin (can carry reverse impulses)

The dome at the base of the fins both rotates them and provides power impulses for the electromotive field

Fins are tough but flexible

BUOYANCY

The sub maintains buoyancy through the use of spongelike hydrostatic chambers. These chambers work like the diving organs of some sea creatures, changing density via the absorption and emission of a heavy oil in a "lifelike" way to control buoyancy and make the sub rise or sink.

Centrifugal pulse conversion electric engine

Engine Noise The sub's electromotive fins make a steady thrum as the vessel moves through the water. Most sea life perceive the sub's noise as a warning to move aside, but the sub's pilot must be wary of large creatures that are far less fearful than they are hungry.

Hydrostatic field receptors

Buoyancy chamber

HYDROSTATIC BUBBLES

The cockpit bubbles of the sub work on the same principle as the bubbles enclosing the underwater city of Otoh Gunga. A hydrostatic field is projected between the prong over each cockpit and the margins where the bubble meets the sub body. The prong and the powerful receptors in the bubble margin act as opposing poles. A force current running between these two poles creates the hydrostatic field of the cockpit bubble that holds air in and keeps water out, while still allowing solid objects to pass through.

Navigational light

Trim control oil cyclers

GUNGAN SUB

This kind of submersible is a common utility transport in Otoh Gunga. The forward cockpit bubble carries only a pilot and passengers, but the side bubbles can carry either passengers or cargo, depending on whether they are fitted with seats. The sub's distinctive form originates from both the Gungans' construction methods and their love of artistic design. The Gungans produce many of their structures using a secret method that actually "grows" the basic skeletons or shells of buildings or vehicles. This gives Gungan constructions a distinctive organic look, which is then complemented by artistic detail, even on simple vehicles like the sub. Gungan organically generated shells can be combined to make complex constructions, and then modified and fitted with electronic and mechanical components to give them the needed functionality. The organic skeletons are exceptionally strong, though still susceptible to damage by some of the larger sea monsters encountered in deep waters.

THE ARM'S-LENGTH RELATIONSHIP

The rectangular cargo containers in the cargo pods of the sub are Naboo-made. While the leaders of Naboo and the Gungans have little contact, out of necessity a significant amount of trade goes on at the fringes of each society, and just as Naboo trade goods are vital in the underwater cities of the Gungans, Gungan products and food supplies are vital to the Naboo people. The two societies pretend not to need each other but are actually greatly intertwined.

Triple-powered hydrostatic bubble projector unit hinges at rear for cargo/passenger loading

Organically generated structural skeleton

Main hydrostatic field generators

Naboo cargo containers

Port cargo bubble

Qui-Gon Jinn

Cockpit bubble

Obi-Wan Kenobi in the pilot's seat

Guidance and control console

Motive field carriers

Control linkage

Starboard hydro-com antenna

Mechanical fittings ducted through organic skeleton

Life-support gear

Jar Jar Binks

Sensor array

Water quality sensors

Forward diving plane is equipped with an electromotive field for greater effectiveness

EXPLORING THE DEEP

While Naboo's landmasses are characterized by lush forests and expansive vistas, the planet's waters are generally considered the stuff of nightmares. Naboo is laced with treacherous underwater tunnels and serpentine caverns that challenge the most experienced pilots of Gungan submersibles, known as bongos. Most of these underwater lanes are filled with monstrous predators, some of which regard wayward bongos as prey. Fortunately, Gungans engineer their bongos with sturdy hulls, powerful electromotive field motors, and headlights that can be adjusted to cut through the murky depths.

Dangerous Tunnels Although naturally formed underwater tunnels offer opportunities for swift travel from one area of Naboo to another, some routes are especially treacherous because of the presence of opee sea killers, whose powerful jaws can rupture a Gungan sub's sturdy hull.

Illuminated Depths While many deep-water fish have naturally evolved phosphorescent appendages to help them lure and locate prey, Gungan subs rely on bright headlights to cut through the murky waters of Naboo.

Expansive View Although the Gungan sub's front seats do not offer much elbow room, the sub's large bubble windows give the impression that the cockpit's space is not so limited.

NAVIGATING THE CORE

Naboo is an ancient and geologically unique world that lacks a molten core, and has numerous swampy lakes on the surface leading deep into the planet's structure. Countless caves and tunnel networks permeate the conglomeration of rocky bodies that make up the planet, and the Gungans have explored and navigated these networks for generations. Despite the risk of run-ins with dangerous aquatic beasts, various networks have come to be regarded as time-honored trade routes, and the most expedient avenues for Gungans to travel from one area of Naboo to another. The region known as the Abyss provides a route between Otoh Gunga and Theed City.

Escape Tactic If an opee sea killer attacks a Gungan sub, the sub's pilot may find help in the form of a gigantic Sando Aqua Monster, which is generally more interested in making a meal of an opee than in any small, passing vessel.

GUNGAN TECHNOLOGY

Thousands of years before the Battle of Naboo, a struggle for territory prompted the Gungans to retreat into the depths of Naboo's seas. There they discovered a strange underwater plant, the locap, which burrows into porous rock and siphons out plasma. The innovative Gungans used subs equipped with front-mounted collectors to harvest plasma from the plant, and discovered many ways to utilize this natural source of energy. The Gungans' distinctive, plasma-based technology is used to generate the hydrostatic fields that surround Gungan cities and submarines.

GUNGAN SUB PEN

To outside eyes a Gungan sub pen might look like an elaborate and beautiful structure of special significance; however, within Otoh Gunga it is just an ordinary docking port. Gungans believe that everything they make speaks of who they are, and that anything they construct should add to the beauty of their world.

Gungan sub in pen

Hydrostatic field generators

Adjustable-Strength Bubbles Obi-Wan and Qui-Gon Jinn pass through the bubble walls of the Gungans' underwater city with relative ease, but the hydrostatic fields that separate air from water can be increased to prevent such passage. The hydrostatic fields on Gungan subs are adjusted to prevent wild creatures from breaking through the field.

Power Controls Despite the sub's resilient construction, being attacked by a large creature can cause damage to the vessel's power units. The power controls are easily accessible to the sub's pilot, and do not require any special knowledge of Gungan electronics to be repaired.

Strong Skeleton Bursting through the sub pen's bubble wall, a Gungan sub instantly enters the sea. The sub's organic skeletal frame is unaffected by the transition from the air-filled sub pen to the sudden water pressure outside.

NABOO QUEEN'S ROYAL STARSHIP

Queen Amidala's Royal Starship is a unique vessel handcrafted by the Theed Palace Space Vessel Engineering Corps. The gleaming craft, usually helmed by the queen's chief pilot, Ric Olié, conveys Queen Amidala in style to locations around Naboo for royal visits, parades, and other duties. The ship also carries Amidala on formal state visits to other planetary rulers or to the Galactic Senate on the capital world of Coruscant. It is designed for short trips, and features limited sleeping facilities, primarily for the ruler and a customary entourage. Expressing the Naboo love of beauty and art, the dreamlike qualities of the ship, together with its extraordinary chromium finish, make it a distinctive presence in any setting. The starship is made to embody the glory of Naboo royalty—service to the queen is a great honor, and to design a Royal Starship is the highest goal to which a Naboo engineer can aspire. Every centimeter of the ship is laid out with exacting precision, making it a true work of art in every respect.

ROYAL CHROMIUM

A mirrored chromium finish gleams over the entire surface of the Royal Starship from stem to stern. Purely decorative, this finish indicates the starship's royal nature. Only the queen's own vessel may be entirely chromed. Royal starfighters are partly chromed, and non-royal Naboo ships bear no chrome at all. The flawless hand-polished chrome surface over the entire Royal Starship is extremely difficult to produce and is executed by traditional craftspeople, not by factory or droid equipment.

NUBIAN AT HEART

The starship's unique spaceframe was manufactured at Theed, yet the ship makes use of many standard galactic high-technology components that cannot be produced on Naboo. The ship is built around elegant Nubian 327 sublight and hyperdrive propulsion system components, giving it high performance and an exotic air. Nubian systems are often sought by galactic royalty and discriminating buyers who appreciate the distinctive design flair of Nubian components. Nubian equipment is easily acquired on civilized worlds but can be hard to obtain on more remote planets, as the queen discovers during her forced landing on Tatooine.

Starboard sensor array dome

Main hold

Tech station

Jar Jar Binks

Elevator to lower deck

Table

Hyperdrive bay (in floor)

Forward hold

Royal quarters

Navigation light recess

Extension boarding ramp to lower deck

Navigation floodlight

Forward maintenance station

Wiring throughout the ship is laid out with exacting care and precision to honor the queen

Power node

Communications antennas

Forward bulkhead

Navigational sensors

Forward long-range sensor array

Forward deflector shield projector

Starboard
deflector shield
generator

Obi-Wan Kenobi

Ric Olié at
pilot's station

Qui-Gon Jinn

Cockpit

Lift

Royal throne
room

Heat-sink
engine finial

Queen Amidala

Droid lift
tube hatch

Audience seats

Sentry

Captain Panaka

Radial sublight
engine

R2-D2   Droid
hold

Landing
gear bay

Portside
sensor array
housing

Droid lift tube

Astromech droid station

Lift to main deck crew
quarters and galley

Circuitry patch bay

Landing gear

Power converters

Fuel lines

Reactant tank

Power
core

Fuel tank

Escape
pod

Portside
deflector shield
projector

Engineering tech
station and override
controls

Stereoscopic
sensor array,
port side

Hyperdrive conduits
channel lightspeed
effect throughout ship

Deflector shield stabilizer

Droids to the Rescue
Astromech droids exit the
aft lift tube hatch to make
emergency repairs to the
Royal Starship's hull and
shield generators. Magnetic
treads keep the droids' feet
secured to the hull, but the
droids are vulnerable to
enemy laserfire.

HYPERDRIVE CORE
Unlike the unruly tangle that complicates the connection
of hyperdrive components in most spacecraft, the queen's
Royal Starship features a hyperdrive core that is an
extraordinary work of precision art. Its intricate maze of
effect channels and charge planes improves the
performance of the hyperdrive to an impressive class 1.8.

THE NABOO WAY
The Royal Starship is completely unarmed in accordance with the Naboo philosophy of
peaceful existence, an ideal growing increasingly rare as undercurrents of discord ripple
through the Galactic Republic. During the Trade Federation invasion of Naboo, the Royal
Starship is the queen's only escape from the occupied palace at Theed, and its exceptional
speed and agility are all it has to evade the deadly blockade around the queen's home planet.

PODRACERS

High-speed Podracing harkens back to primitive eras with its traditional podracer designs and the mortal danger seen in racing spectacles. Pulled on flexible control cables by fearsomely powerful independent engines, a small open cockpit (the "pod") carries a daring pilot at speeds that can exceed 800 kilometers (500 miles) per hour. Considered in its lightning-fast modern form too much for humans to manage, Podracing is almost exclusively carried on by other species that sport more limbs, more durable bodies, a wider range of sensory organs, or other biological advantages.

THE STORY OF THE SPORT

Podracing has its origins in ancient contests of animal-drawn carts, of the kind still seen in extremely primitive systems far from the space lanes. Long ago a daring mechanic called Phoebos recreated the old arrangement with repulsorlift pods and flaming jet engines for a whole new level of competition and risk. The famous first experimental race ensured Podracing's reputation as an incredibly dangerous and popular sport.

Starting Grid When podracers line up on the arena's starting grid, some pilots deliberately position their vehicles so the heat from their engines will hamper the path or vision of the pilots behind them.

TEEMTO'S PODRACER

Teemto Pagalies' podracer is typical of podracers found in the Outer Rim: a unique design incorporating certain standard features. Its unusual circular shape is designed around an internal metal cycling ring which acts as a gyroscopic stabilizer for the non-aerodynamic pod. Other components are standard: control line anchors, a brace of repulsors to float the podracer safely off the ground, a complex engine sensor and telemetry computer package, and a variety of control levers and switches suited to the particular body shape of the race pilot himself.

> ## "Very fast, very dangerous."
> Qui-Gon Jinn

Air exhaust

Rudder mount

Rudder axis

Racing decor

Rudder actuator; tail rudder provides steering control

Gyro ring power unit

Gyro ring drive electromagnets pulse in sequence to rotate mass ring for stability, keeping pod upright

Air cleaner

Computer
power unit

Gyro ring channel;
ring rotates within
it at 230 rpm

Multi-computer
sensor-processor
package

Sensor readouts

Main throttle

Power
steering
servo
assembly

Driver seat

Control cable
tensioner

Control cable
transmitter

Ring drive magnet heat vent

"Floater" mid-power repulsorlifts
keep pod off the ground

Left control cable

Right control cable
insulation wrapping

Control cable
shock absorber

THE RACE LINEUP

Racers qualify for starting positions at the Mos Espa arena via a complex set of traditions
that involve a combination of past performance, popularity, and random chance. Most
podracers feature a distinctive ensign or decor scheme representing a race pilot's rich patron,
family lineage, protective deity, supporting guild, or simply colors that appeal to them.
Colorful flags bearing these emblems herald the beginning of the formal race ceremony,
and dynamic racing graphics decorate the vehicles for visibility and good luck. As with the
podracer designs, the bewildering variety of ensign types seen at Mos Espa arena contributes
to the dazzling spectacle of the races.

Pit Hangar Constructed on
Malastare and shipped to Tatooine
at great expense by Jabba the Hutt,
Mos Espa arena's pit hangar is
designed to accommodate dozens
of podracers and their teams.
Pit droids and mechanics use
overhead cranes to lift and move
podracers when their repulsorlifts
are powered down.

PODRACING TODAY

Long ago banned from most civilized systems, Podracing is still
famous on Malastare and in a few other locales. Real Podracing
aficionados, however, look beyond the Republic to the rugged worlds
of the Outer Rim, where podraces still serve as a spectacle for
hundreds of thousands and vast gambling fortunes are made and lost.
This naturally makes the Hutts an accessory to most racing venues.

THE BOONTA EVE CLASSIC

Eighteen podracers, many of them well known, qualify for the great Boonta Eve Race in which nine-year-old Anakin Skywalker enters his customized Radon-Ulzer. Also known as the Boonta Eve Classic, the race is held at Mos Espa on Tatooine, and is the largest annual Podrace in the galaxy. The Boonta's racecourse features terrifying drops and tortuous curves that pose deadly challenges even to veteran competitors. Notoriously fine-tuned machines, not all the podracers make it as far as the starting line—and several more never make it to the finish—for while mechanical breakdowns are not uncommon, the high-stakes Boonta is also menaced by discreet sabotage.

Ark Roose's Plug-G 927 Ark "Bumpy" Roose is towed by twin-turbined Vokoff-Strood Plug-8G Cluster Array engines with a top speed of 775 kilometers per hour. The open-air channel in the center of each engine cluster provides excellent cooling.

Scale in meters
(5 m = 16½ ft)
0   5

ARK "BUMPY" ROOSE

RATTS TYERELL

BEN QUADINAROS

ODY MANDRELL

ELAN MAK

EBE ENDOCOTT

ANAKIN SKYWALKER

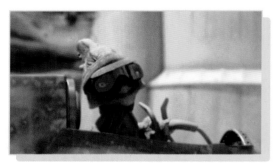

Ratts Tyerell's *Scatalpen* Named after a deadly predator from his homeworld, Tyerell's *Scatalpen* uses twin Vokoff-Strood Titan 2150 rocket engines to tow it to a top speed of 841 kilometers per hour.

Anakin Skywalker's 620C A pair of modified Radon-Ulzer 620C racing engines tows the podracer built by Tatooine native Anakin Skywalker. Although Anakin is strong for a boy his size, he has adjusted his podracer's controls to compensate for his comparatively limited strength.

Ben Quadinaros' BT310 A Toong from the planet Tund, Ben is the least qualified pilot to enter the Boonta. Although his rented Balta-Trabaat BT310 podracer can reach 940 kilometers per hour, its power couplings fail just as the race starts.

Gasgano's *Ord Pedrovia* A six-armed Xexto, Gasgano built his podracer from scratch. Named the *Ord Pedrovia*, his pod has customized anti-turbulence vanes and thrust stabilizer cones on the engines, which propel the craft at speeds of up to 820 kilometers per hour.

Dud Bolt's Vulptereen 327 Dud Bolt pilots a Vulptereen 327 that was manufactured on his homeworld, the planet Vulpter. Identified in some racing manuals as the RS 557, the Vulptereen 327 is very sturdy, has great traction, and can achieve a top speed of 760 kilometers per hour.

Teemto Pagalies' LongTail A Veknoid from Moonus Mandel, Teemto Pagalies pilots an IPG-X1131 LongTail manufactured by Irdani Performance Group. The LongTail has a maximum speed of 775 kilometers per hour, and offers excellent traction on the twisting race course.

Sebulba's Plug-F Mammoth An arboreal Dug, Sebulba is the favorite to win the Boonta Eve Classic, and he is determined to use every dirty trick he knows to make his fans happy. The primary controls for his Plug-F Mammoth are designed so he can operate them with his dexterous feet.

Scale in meters
(5 m = 16½ ft)

0   5

GASGANO

DUD BOLT

WAN SANDAGE

CLEGG HOLDFAST

NEVA KEE

BOLES ROOR

MAWHONIC

MARS GUO

ALDAR BEEDO

TEEMTO PAGALIES

SEBULBA

WINNING, SEBULBA STYLE

Sebulba is maniacally driven to win, and his determination goes further than exceeding race rules on his engine parameters and threatening race officials who ask too many questions. Whispered rumors in the pits describe weapons built into Sebulba's engines. At the 800 kph (500 mph) speeds of Podracing, who can tell what is really happening way out there on the flats and in the canyons? So far his crimes have gone unpunished. Sebulba has been accused before, but his engines always seem to be clean when officials demand an inspection. Different systems made to be removable keep the wily Dug from being caught for his murderous cheating. At present, his primary weapon is a flame emitter, which fries competitors' engines.

Rear-View Sensors In Sebulba's podracer, a sensor scope displays an aft-camera view of Mars Guos' podracer as it approaches fast from behind.

Telemetry and control console

Sebulba

Mini-inertial compensator

Control power generator

Control linkage

Repulsorlift generator

Anakin Skywalker

Throttle levers

Podracer telemetry computers use sensor data to calculate ideal pressure and temperature algorithms

Air scoops

Flame emitter weapon

Control pod

Cockpit computer requires a special power cell that delivers a high-voltage filtered electronic power feed

Afterburner heat dissipator fins

Control linkage

Steelton control cable

Afterburner fuel tanks

Tri-carbon anti-turbulence vanes

Fuel injector ring

Combustion chamber and direct variable air inlet

Thrust stabilizer cone

Thrust ring

Energy binder plate

Fuel lines

Spill air doors

Fuel atomizer/ distributors

Fuel injector nozzles

Core fuel tank

8-stage main compressor

ANAKIN'S CREATION

Anakin made his engines from salvaged Radon-Ulzer racing engines that Watto regarded as too burned-out to be worth keeping. Anakin did a great deal of rewiring and re-routed the fuel distribution, adding a whole new subsystem that injects much more fuel throughout the combustion sequence, to develop far greater thrust.

Primary intake turbine

Turbine drive motor

Turbine drive energizer

Triple air scoops

Over-pressure system valve

PODRACING RIVALS

The great Boonta Eve Race on Tatooine is a legend among podracers. It is here that racers congregate from widespread star systems to match their skills and their engines against the best, in a setting largely unrefined by civilized society or its rules. Here are to be seen the most determined racers, the most extreme power ratios, the most exciting experimental engines that would be illegal elsewhere, and the most underhanded tactics to be found in the sport. And it is on this stage that a nine-year-old boy named Anakin Skywalker faces the highest possible stakes with a podracer he built himself.

Engine fuel
igniters

Excess air
vent fan

Excess air
spill door

Radiator
hoses

Annular
fuel tank

Compressor

Energy
binder plate

Fuel
injector

Combustion
chamber

Coolant pump

Energy
binder arc

Coolant
radiators

Airflow
director
fence

Split-X repulsor
generator housing

Energy binder
generator

Upper Split-X
air intake

Split-X stabilizing
vane

SIZE AND PERFORMANCE

Most podracers go for greater power through greater size, exploiting loopholes in the racing rules to enter larger and more powerful engines with tacked-on subsystems to increase their performance. Sebulba's engines are barely within the rules and would probably not hold up to close inspection, but the race referees know better than to press the issue too hard with the evil Dug. Anakin's engines are remarkable in that he has derived incredible performance from engines smaller than everything else currently used. It all comes from his radical fuel atomizer and distribution system, with multiple igniters throughout the system to get maximum burn from every atom of fuel. In effect, the whole engine is an afterburner once it gets going, but the system works on extremely delicate balances and can be flooded with fuel if pushed before the engines are going full bore, as Anakin finds out early on in the race.

"It's Skywalker! The crowds are going nuts!"

Fodesinbeed Annodue

CATCHING THE WIND

One of Anakin's cleverest engine modifications is the set of triple air scoops ranged around each primary turbine intake. These "air brakes" provide additional control in cornering. Anakin had to wait a long time before he found metal plates and a hydraulic system that would be strong enough to make this idea work. The hydraulic struts are of Tyrian manufacture and came from a military surplus lot that Watto bought from Dreddon the Hutt, a crimelord known to make many arms deals in the lawless star systems of the Outer Rim.

Engine Readout Anakin has modified his podracer's computer to give detailed readouts of energy fluctuations, allowing him to make swift adjustments to his engines.

TOOLS OF EVIL

Built beneath the invisibility field projector are compartments containing equipment for Darth Maul's missions. Floating "dark eye" probe droids, a speeder bike, interrogator droids, prisoner torture devices, spying and surveillance gear, bombs, mines and eavesdropping technology are only part of the Sith Lord's inventory, and Darth Maul is never at a loss for equipment. Sith training has made Maul less reliant on technology and stronger in his inner abilities, but he keeps his Infiltrator fully equipped with the most advanced technology to maximize his power.

THE INVISIBLE ENEMY

Invisibility fields were considered theoretical until the discovery of the rare stygium crystals on the volcanically turbulent planet Aeten II in the Outer Rim. An invisibility field is a terrifying weapon, since it can defeat most security systems and make acts of theft, sabotage, and assassination all but unstoppable.

Cloak field generator

Cloak generator hood

Stygium crystal mounts

Darth Maul's speeder bike is deployed through the underside cargo hatch

Storage for poisons, deadly weapons, blades, and other devices of evil intent

Swing bin

Access channel to cloak field generator and portions of cargo bay

"Dark eye" probe droids are remotely activated

Cargo drop panel folds down to allow access to stored items

Landing gear

Radiator panels

Overload cache

SITH INFILTRATOR

During their long centuries of secret actions against the Jedi Order, Sith apprentices have maintained a tradition of special spacecraft suited to their evil missions, called Sith Infiltrators. Darth Maul's dreaded craft, the *Scimitar*, is the latest in this ancient line of dark vessels and is perhaps the most dangerous Infiltrator yet created. Able to appear and disappear with the ease of a shadow, it hides in its distinctive long prow a formidable full-effect cloaking device, a technological wonder that gives it invisibility on command. The Infiltrator is a customized version of an advanced armed star courier design from the workshop of the technological genius Raith Sienar, and features laser cannons, extensive sensor systems, and an experimental high-temperature ion engine system requiring large radiator panels, which fold inward during landings. Darth Maul uses the powerful capabilities of his Infiltrator to learn secret information, plan sabotage, and track targeted individuals anywhere in the galaxy. This evasive and deadly craft is an appropriate extension of the uncanny abilities of its Sith Lord pilot.

DROID STARFIGHTER

The space fighters deployed from the Trade Federation battleships are themselves droids, not piloted by any living being. Showered upon enemies in tremendous swarms, droid starfighters—also known as Vulture droids—dart through space in maddening fury, elusive targets and deadly opponents for living defenders. They are controlled by a continuously modulated signal from the central Droid Control Ship computer, which tracks every single fighter just as it pulses through the processor of every single battle droid. The signal receiver and onboard computer brain is in the "head" of the fighter and twin sensor pits serve as "eyes."

Composite shell covers antenna that receives control signal

Retracted walk mode claws

Landing repulsor bands

Thrust exhaust nozzles

ATTACK AND FLIGHT MODES

Vulture droids are the most sophisticated automated starfighters ever built, carrying four laser cannons as well as two energy torpedo launchers, which gives them firepower far beyond their size class. To both protect and conceal its deadly laser cannons, the droid starfighter retracts its wings in flight mode (above). In this configuration, the droid can hide its military nature, enabling it to ambush the unwary. Covering the weapons when not in use also shields them from micro-particles and atmospheric corrosion. This can improve their accuracy by a tiny degree, an effort at high precision typical of the Haor Chall Engineering company.

Active sensor "eyes" use long-wavelength radiation to find targets

Visual sensors

Primary sensor ports

Magnetic imaging sensors

Droid brain components

Antenna

Energy torpedo firing channels angled for anti-personnel use in walk mode

Pneumatic system power converter

Electric screwjack

Extended scissor action walk mode claw

Laser retraction motor

Repulsor projectors allow soft landings

Neck strut deploys head forward in walk mode

Laser power converters

Laser power cells

Power pulse cycling circuitry

Hydraulic system sump

Pneumatic system charge cylinder

Claw angle adjust ram/ shock absorbers

WALKING FIGHTERS

When they land on enemy territory, droid starfighters reconfigure themselves into walk patrol mode, using antigravity repulsors to drop safely to the ground. Droid starfighters can thus serve as guards to territory they have blasted into submission. In walk patrol mode they can launch into the air to pursue fleeing ships as easily as they can gun down resisting populations of "future customers." Unsettling, ungainly, and towering, they evoke terror as well as carrying firepower. A droid starfighter in walk patrol mode presents an eerie spectacle: a mindless killing machine directed by a far-off intelligence.

DROID CONTROL SHIP

From the very first stages, the Trade Federation armaments committee planned to make use of their commercial fleet of giant cargo ships to transport weapons of war. Familiar to millions of officials and civilian personnel, the characteristic Trade Federation cargo ships had been built over many years, plying cargo among the far-flung stars of the galaxy as part of their extensive market. These seemingly harmless and slow-moving container ships would now hide, deep within their hangars, the secret army built to change the rules of commerce. By the end of the project's construction phase the Neimoidians had created from them a frightening fleet of battleships.

WAR CONVERSIONS

The converted battleships bear unusual equipment for cargo freighters, including powerful quad laser batteries designed to destroy opposition fighters launched against the secret army transports. These batteries are built to rotate inward while not in use, concealing their true nature until the Neimoidians wish to uncloak their military intentions to unsuspecting "future customers." While the cargo hangars and their ceiling racks in the inner hangar zones proved sufficient for the carriage of the secret army ground forces, additional large electrified racks were installed in the outermost hangar zones to quarter the dangerous colonies of droid starfighters, which draw power from the racks until launch.

CIVILIAN COMPROMISES

While the Trade Federation cargo fleet was ideal for hiding the existence of the secret army and carrying it unobtrusively to points of deployment, the commercial origins of the battleships leave them with shortcomings as "battleships." Fitted with numerous guns around the equatorial bands, the battleships carry considerable firepower with very limited coverage and so large areas of the ship are undefended by emplaced artillery. The onboard swarms of droid starfighters are thus essential for defense of the battleships from fighter attack.

Tractor array power system

Hull strengthened with irregular armor plating

Starboard hangar arm

Scanner array

Giant inertial compensator prevents acceleration damage

Primary drive engines

Secondary drive engine

Centersphere

THE HAND BEHIND THE SECRET ARMY

While the Trade Federation has long been known as a greedy and conniving organization of merchants, the use of armed force to increase its profits hardly befits its cowardly nature. A strange force has been at work, making the Trade Federation capable of extraordinary measures and setting it on a path of conflict that will shake the Galactic Republic to its core.

Hangars within the inner wall provide docking space for shuttles carrying officials, trade diplomats, merchants, and bureaucrats

Secondary docking arms of several types support docking maneuvers with a wide variety of cargo craft

Main tractor beam generator

Multiple tractor beam projectors guide craft of various sizes into safe landing in the outer hangar

Hangar landing target provides signal for automatic docking of visiting spacecraft

Reinforced bracing for primary docking claw

Primary docking claw rotator assembly

C-9979 landing ship, still under guidance from docking tractor beam array, starts onboard full propulsion at this point

Primary docking claws lock onto colossal freight barges for cargo transfer

Rotators allow quad lasers to be withdrawn for concealment

Quad laser batteries in firing position

Armored, sealed hangars hold shipments of highly toxic or dangerous materials stored well away from main hangar zones

Extensive deck structure within centersphere provides quarters a offices for Neimoidian population their trade partners

Portside main hangar portals

Docking tractor beam housing

Fully loaded landing ship in launch-ready sequence

Outer hangar (zone 1) landing area. Landing ships stage here for launch

Typical triple quad laser battery

Cargo bays lining hangar walls built for holding shipments of galactic cargo

Turbolaser Batteries Each Control Ship has 42 quad turbolaser emplacements. As sensors track enemy vessels, the Control Ship's computers automatically adjust the turrets to fire at the most strategic targets.

The *Scimitar* Darth Maul guides his Sith Infiltrator, which has been named the *Scimitar*, to Tatooine in search of the elusive Queen Amidala and her Jedi escorts.

Radiator fin (open)

Waste energy phasing node

Power cell array

Control console

Maul's seat

Inertial compensator (ring type)

Lift

Radiator fin (closed)

Passenger seats

High temperature ion drive circuitry

Thrust trace dampers

Sublight engines

Heat and radiation exchange system

Power cells

Extensive power cell array

Darth Maul

UNORTHODOX TECHNOLOGY

The armed courier upon which the Infiltrator was based is a development of Raith Sienar's Advanced Projects laboratory, which continues to experiment with unorthodox spacecraft technologies. Sienar's designs typically incorporate weapons even in craft made for peaceful purposes.

SIENAR: LEGACY AND DESTINY

It is sometimes darkly hinted that Raith Sienar is poised to design the deadly spacecraft of a new space navy that would enforce the law of a new order in the galaxy. In fact, Raith Sienar's operations will eventually become Sienar Fleet Systems, famous and feared throughout the galaxy in the days of the Empire. Sienar's Advanced Projects laboratory will one day create a distinctive TIE fighter reminiscent of the Infiltrator, which will be used by Maul's successor, Darth Vader.

High-speed drive engine

Steering handle

Accelerator pedal

SPEEDER BIKE

Unarmed, this speeder's only special equipment is a high-acceleration engine enabling the bike to reach amazing speeds and cut tight corners. The open design gives excellent visibility.

Hunter in the Desert
Having tracked his prey to Tatooine, Darth Maul rides his speeder bike to confront the Jedi who protect the queen.

Lethal Precision Weaving across space in tight, rapid formations, droid starfighters have a deadly advantage over living opponents.

Engine module as removed for refueling

Thrust dampers electromagnetically vector propulsion

Solid fuel slug chamber

Engine cooling fins

Solid fuel slug

Hydraulic wing/leg extension system

Thrust exhaust nozzles

Walking leg struts (retracted)

Hydraulic and pneumatic charging systems for wing deployment and leg walking movement

Energy torpedo cannon

Antigravity generator

Power converter

Internal system cooling unit and demagnetizer

Flight assault lasers

Laser muzzle brake

Permanently installed power cells are recharged while droid is locked into war freighter power grid

Light non-magnetic alclad alloy plating

DROID STARFIGHTER COLONY STORAGE

Dense ranks of droid starfighters hang from ceiling girders in the outer hangar zone of Trade Federation battleships, stored out of the way of hangar activities. Connected to a high-voltage power grid, the droid starfighters quietly hum as they are charged to maximum capacity by the reactors of the host battleship. Individual fighters periodically test their systems as they hang, flexing their wings and turning their heads, presenting the uncanny impression of a colony of flying cave predators lying in wait.

AMAZING PRECISION

The flying, walking, shape-shifting droid starfighter requires extremely specialized manufacturing, of the kind found in the cathedral factories of the Xi Char, founders of Hoar Chall Engineering. There, ultra-precision manufacturing is a religious practice followed by thousands. The initiates do not concern themselves with the ultimate use of their deadly creations, making the Xi Char ideal pawns of the Trade Federation's dark purposes.

SOLID FIRE FUEL

Unconventional solid fuel concentrate slugs give droid starfighters their powerful thrust. Expensive to manufacture, the slugs burn furiously when ignited, allowing the droid starfighter to hurtle through space with minimal engine mass. Thrust streams are vectored electromagnetically for steering. The solid fuel system limits the droids' fighting time, but the numerous droids are easily recycled back into their racks for recharge and refueling when spent.

Transmission tower antennae broadcast the vital droid control signal sustaining the mechanized army

Primary sensor rectenna

Auxiliary sensor rectennas

Exotic composite alloys allow transmission antennas to withstand extremely high signal strength

Multiple high-energy transmission towers tap main reactors for broadcast power

Transmitter platform defense artillery

Signal transmitter platform

Primary drive engine thrust chamber

Portside main reactor

Landing ship pedestals in ceiling racks

Landing ship fuselage in ceiling rack

Pilot reactor heads

Signal pickup boost panels squelch noise and interference

Pilot reactor fuel pumps and pressure stabilizer assembly

Midline defense batteries

Cranes assist in assembly of landing ship components

Inner hangar (zone 3). Landing ship components are assembled here

Sliding hangar zone bulkhead doors

Assembled landing ship prepares to enter zone 2

Underside droid signal receiver station

Hangar atmosphere ducting

Starboard Main Reactor Two main reactors are housed in the port and starboard hangar arms respectively. Their powerful shields and fortified locations make the Neimoidians confident that the reactors cannot be breached by enemy fire.

THE DROID CONTROL SHIP

The single critically important vessel among the Trade Federation fleet of battleships is the Droid Control Ship. Custom-fitted with massive transmitters, receiver antennae, monitor sensors, and numerous additional reactors and power substations to run them, the Droid Control Ship contains tremendous computer banks and the Control Brain Network, which transmits the signals vital to the functioning of every battle droid in the Trade Federation army. From this one Droid Control Ship is broadcast the control signals that direct each droid's actions, making up for the very limited onboard logic systems of the minimalist droids. Without this constant signal and its stabilizing carrier wave, the battle droids would be useless "terminals," incapable of independent action or self-control.

Primary Target Knowing that destroying the Control Ship is the key to defeating the droid forces on Naboo, pilots of the Naboo Space Fighter Corps concentrate their attacks on the vessel.

Droid signal receiver station

Backup sensor rectenna

Forward control tower

Droid control computer core

Computer core temperature control system

Control computer core power distribution monitoring stations

Control bridge tower

Array of 16 droid signal receiver stations pick up the many thousands of signals sent for processing by the main droid control computer

Backup control signal transmission towers

Zone 3 inner wall hangar

Deflector shield generator housing

Deflector shield projectors

Main droid control computer support systems

Centersphere reactors

droid starfighters locked into roof power grids

Hangar zone bulkhead

MTTs being loaded into C-9979 landing ship

Landing ship being fully loaded with ground troops and armor

MTTs staged for loading

AATs await loading

Ground armor long-term storage in subfloor garages

Massive ammunition dumps

Middle hangar (zone 2). Landing ships are loaded and armed here

A PILOT'S BEST FRIEND

The onboard astromech droid, a standard R2 type, performs in-flight systems management and flight performance optimization as well as offering limited repair capabilities. The pilot-droid configuration has long proven ideal for small space fighter craft and will continue to do so for generations to come.

Power charge collector

Accidental Pilot Anakin Skywalker takes cover inside the cockpit of a Naboo starfighter to avoid being shot by battle droids. But when the starfighter's autopilot kicks in, Anakin and R2-D2 are whisked into space.

ART AND DESIGN

While the long "rat-tail" finials projecting from the engines may look like design flourishes, they are in fact part of the customized engine system developed by the Theed Palace engineers. The finials are actually heat sinks, which circulate coolant and help dissipate the excessive heat of the Nubian engines. The customized Naboo engine configuration burns hotter than normal so as to burn more cleanly, since the Naboo people are very careful not to pollute their planet's environment. The necessary heat sinks were configured into the elegant finials—an example of the inspiring combination of art and engineering found in the best Naboo design work.

Battle computer interface

Electromagnetic signal receiver

R2 unit computer

R2 astromech droid: the ship's computer and systems plug into the droid's head and body from within

Windshield (slides forward for boarding)

Anakin Skywalker

Power node

Inertial compensator

R2 unit leg clamps

To fit into the small N-1's droid socket, the onboard R2 unit is loaded into the fighter from below. The droid's legs telescope into themselves slightly, and then the droid's head telescopes upward from his body to appear at the back of the fighter

Life-support systems

Power cells

Landing gear

Heat sink finial

Engine heat sink

Customized high-temperature combustion chamber

Engine-bearing structural member

Fuel lines

Ionization chamber

Sensor lines

Pressure manifold

Binocular rangefinders, targeting, and flight sensors

HIGH-VOLTAGE RAT-TAIL

The center "rat-tail" finial projecting from the rear of the N-1 is a vital component, linking the ship to the palace hangar systems via a plug-in socket found at the rear of each ship's protective revetment area. The primary purpose of this finial is to receive high-voltage power charge energy delivered from the palace generators to activate the ship's systems. Large transformers and converters can be seen on either side of the plug-in sockets in the fighter revetment. The secondary purpose of the center finial is to receive coded information from the palace battle computer. This computer will download information only in the primary security room and through these fighter sockets, preventing any spies from being able to acquire battle information from the palace. The palace battle computer transfers complete battle coordinates and strategic plans into each fighter, allowing the pilots to concentrate on operating their ship's systems while the flight computer automatically directs the ship on a trajectory to the target zone.

NABOO N-1 STARFIGHTER

The single pilot Naboo Royal N-1 starfighter was developed by the Theed Palace Space Vessel Engineering Corps for the volunteer Royal Naboo Security Forces. Sleek and agile, the small N-1 faces aggressors with twin blaster cannons and a double magazine of proton torpedoes. Found only on Naboo and rarely seen even there, the N-1, like the queen's Royal Starship, uses many galactic standard internal components in a custom-built spaceframe that reflects the Naboo people's love of handcrafted, elegant shapes. The Naboo engineers fabricate some of their own parts, such as fuel tanks and sensor antennae, but most of the high-technology gear is acquired through trade from other, more industrialized worlds. The Theed Palace engineers developed a customized engine system, however, based on a standard Nubian drive motor but modified significantly to release fewer emissions into the atmosphere.

Laser fire control processor

Laser stabilizing field generator prevents unstable laser bolts from backfiring and damaging the ship

Laser cannon

THAT GLEAMING ROYAL LOOK

The N-1 fighter sports a gleaming chromium finish on its forward surfaces, indicating the ship's royal status. Early Naboo spacecraft required a chromelike finish for protection from harmful rays in the planet's upper atmosphere. Now that spacecraft and their pilots are fully shielded from such rays by electromagnetic field technology, the chrome finish is retained for tradition and kept as a royal symbol. Only royal ships may carry the hand-finished royal chromium treatment.

Receiver

Communications antennas

Royal chromium finish

Fuel pumps and hydraulic system pressurizer

Torpedo launcher assembly

Torpedo magazine (ship carries twin magazines of 5 torpedoes each)

Proton torpedo

Torpedo firing chamber chargers

Infiltrating the Droid Control Ship
After R2-D2 disables the Naboo starfighter's autopilot, Anakin takes evasive action and pilots the fighter into the Trade Federation's Droid Control Ship.

Protective nacelle dome

DEFENDERS OF NABOO

Because the Naboo are peaceful people, the Space Fighter Corps is maintained as much through tradition as for military defense, primarily serving as an honor guard for the queen's Royal Starship. Nonetheless, the Royal Naboo Security Forces train in their N-1s on a regular basis, prepared for the honor of serving the queen in combat if necessary, since service to the queen symbolizes service to the great free people of Naboo themselves. When the Trade Federation invades Naboo, the pilots of the Space Fighter Corps know that they must fight against tremendous odds if they are to free their planet.

Chromium Distraction While the N-1 starfighter's chromium finish identifies the ship's royal status, the highly reflective surfaces also serve to "dazzle" enemies, who must adjust their optical sensors to focus on the N-1.

Hyperdrive

Rear center finial plugs into socket in fighter revetment

Fuel tank

Evasive Maneuvers Engaged in their first space battle, Naboo pilots rely on years of training and experience with simulation exercises to avoid being shot down by enemy fire.

STAP

The Single Trooper Aerial Platform (STAP) is an agile flying conveyance designed for Trade Federation battle droids, and outwardly similar to individual repulsorlift "airhooks" used for civilian and military purposes throughout the galaxy. Able to travel swiftly and through dense vegetation, the STAP performs scouting and anti-personnel hunting missions in support of main battle force actions. High-voltage energy cells power the compact machine for limited deployment sorties, after which they must return to be recharged.

Protect the Landing Zone Droid invasion forces are at their most vulnerable as they unload from their invasion transports. STAPs are therefore quickly and easily deployed to patrol the landing zones.

Elevated Position STAP-mounted battle droids serve as roving "eyes" for the Droid Control Ship to help determine battlefield maneuvers.

Battle droid with blaster

B1 Battle Droids After the Trade Federation's invasion of Naboo, battle droid scouts fly STAPs over Naboo's Great Grass Plains to survey the terrain, and transmit data to the Droid Control ship.

Twin blasters

Blaster energizer

Drive turbines

Power cell housing

Footlocks

Antigravity projector

AAT

Designed and built by the Baktoid Armor Workshop for the Trade Federation secret army, the AAT (Armored Assault Tank) carries a crew of four battle droids into combat, presenting the enemy with a heavily armored facade and a blistering hail of assault fire from five laser guns and six energy shell launchers. Their deployment on Naboo is their first use in open combat, but the tanks have seen considerable training action, leaving them scarred and weathered. The AAT is designed for head-on combat in formal battle lines and is accordingly very heavily armored up front. In fact, the nose of the AAT is almost solid armor, designed to crash through heavy walls with impunity.

INSIDE THE COCKPIT

A droid pilot guides the AAT and provides targeting information to the two gunners. The pilot uses a stereoscopic camera that relays information to a periscope scanner.

Secondary laser gun

Rangefinders

Primary laser cannon

Up to six ground troop battle droids can ride into battle using the three handholds on either side of the tank body

Front hatch: pilot can open it for direct visual sighting if camera damaged

AAT pilot

Capture of Theed As the most heavily armed ground vehicles in the Trade Federation's invasion force, AATs lead the advance on the capital city of Naboo.

Air cooling intake

Short-range blaster

Auxiliary status readouts

Shell launcher armor plate

"Foot" section nose ram

ENERGY SHELLS

The AAT's six shell launch tubes can be equipped with a range of ammunition types. As they are launched, the shells are cocooned in high-energy plasma. This speeds them on their way by reducing friction, and dramatically improves their penetrating power. AATs can be prepared for specialized missions with particular shell loads.

Heavy solid plate armor

Forward repulsor disc

Bunker-busting shells

Armor-piercing shells

Energy cocooning chamber

Launch tube

Top hatch

Tank commander in
seated position

Laser charge
battery

Main cannon
elevator

Control
command
receiver
antennas

Battlefield
sensors

Turret rotation
motor

Turret rotation
pedals

Power generator

Main
hatchway

Power converter
(very hot)

Left gunner

Exit ramp

Repulsor coils

General purpose
high-energy shells

Heavy Bombardment AAT laser cannons fire
at Gungan forces during the Battle of Naboo.

POWER PLANT

The reactor and key power and communications gear are kept
to the rear for protection. Heavy-duty repulsors (both disc and
coils) keep the AAT just off the ground and propel it forward.

Four-chambered
multi-reactor
power plant

"Open fire!"

Battle Droid Commander

EXPLOSIVE COMBINATION

The three ammunition types carried as standard-issue
ordnance on the AAT include "bunker buster" high explosives,
armor-piercing shells, and standard high-energy shells for
anti-personnel and anti-vehicle use.

"Bunker-buster"
high explosive shell

Armor-piercing
shell

High-energy
shell

ENERGY SHELL MAGAZINES

The AAT's energy shells cannot be replenished by the droid
crew on board. Instead, the shells are reloaded when the tank
returns to a landing ship or battleship, where mechanical
facilities take the entire contents of the "foot" off the tank
from below. A loaded replacement is then installed in its place.

NABOO SPEEDERS

The small ground craft of the Naboo Royal Security volunteers are lightly armed and armored, since they patrol a fairly peaceful society. They are designed for rapid pursuit and capture of troublemakers, rather than combat with an armed enemy. The Flash and Gian speeders are the most common Naboo ground security craft. Both patrol vehicles are sturdy and reliable and bear mounts for laser weapons that are sent into action only when such force is absolutely necessary.

FLASH SPEEDERS

One of several small ground vehicles used by the Royal Naboo Security Forces, the Flash landspeeder is designed for street patrol and high-speed pursuit of malefactors. The craft normally flies less than a meter off the ground and at maximum height can attain a "float" of a couple of meters.

Urban Patrols The Flash speeder is an agile, general-use craft with thrust engines finely tuned to give the pilot good control on narrow city streets.

- Engine cowling
- Mount post keeps blaster above heads of occupants
- Pursuit/defense blaster
- Targeting rangefinder
- Generator cooling channel
- Accessory mount spoiler
- Power and fuel lines
- 360° swivel mount
- Wing-mounted thrust pod improves maneuverability
- Pilot
- Windshield
- Aerodynamic streamlined nose
- Starboard power generator
- Triple drive turbines
- Drive turbine air intake
- Systems computer
- Repulsor projector
- Protector plate
- Lateral repulsor bank
- Fuel tank
- Basic floor construction designed for urban use
- Main power cable
- Throttle controls

ESCAPING THE TRADE FEDERATION

In the terrible conflict with the Trade Federation, Flash speeders make good use of their well-known speed and maneuverability as they spirit Naboo resistance fighters quickly to and from secret rendezvous points beyond the eyes of patrolling battle droids and droid starfighters.

- Medium-grade hull plating
- Seating for two observers or specialists
- Pilot
- Thrust pods tucked in to reduce target silhouette
- Gunner
- Laser generator/capacitor assembly
- Light repeater laser blaster
- Auxiliary power unit for each gun

GIAN SPEEDERS

Gian speeders are heavier vehicles than the Flash speeders and are called out only for serious situations. Their three laser blasters can easily disable non-military vehicles. They have tougher hulls than ordinary civilian craft and their reinforced bodies allow them to withstand glancing hits. Their compact forward silhouette, with thrust pods tucked in behind rather than out on wing struts, makes the Gian less maneuverable but a harder target for enemies both in front and behind. To assist in tactical deployments, these speeders can be equipped with customized holographic planning systems.

CORUSCANT TAXI

The air taxi shooting through the vast open spaces between the high skyscrapers is one of the most characteristic sights of the famous metropolis world of Coruscant. These air taxis are allowed unrestricted "free travel" and can thus leave the autonavigating skylanes to take the most direct routes to their destination. Skylanes confine most vehicles on long-distance journeys along defined corridors, without which there would be unmanageable chaos in the air. To rate "free travel," air taxi pilots must pass demanding tests that prove their ability to navigate the unique cityscape with skill and safety. They depend on their scanners, keen eyes, and instinct to avoid crashing into other craft, sending their passengers plunging into the street canyons far below.

Convenient Transport Manufactured by the Hyrotti Corporation, the EasyRide passenger airspeeder is the company's most common model.

Communications antenna

Efficient drive engine requires a minimum of fuel

Forward motion engine

Turbine allows rapid acceleration

Guidance computer balances navigational control between lift repulsors, steering repulsors, and drive engines

Luggage can be stored in crossbar compartments

Seats emit mild tractor field in flight to hold passengers securely inside without belts

Headlight circuitry varies spectrum output of beams

Drive engine housing

Multi-spectrum headlights

Simple construction designed for easy maintenance and repair

Side-mounted, low-power repulsors prevent collision and cushion docking

Signal receivers built into body frame pick up air traffic control transmissions

Lift repulsor carries taxi to great skyscraper heights

Precision stabilizing and steering radial repulsor array helps taxi navigate in crowded urban skylanes

WELL-EQUIPPED AIR TAXIS

The standard modern Coruscant air taxi uses a compact, focused, medium-grade repulsor to elevate it to the very highest skyscraper peaks. A radial battery of lower-powered antigravity devices gives it good navigational control in the open air, allowing it to swoop with accuracy around the aerial architecture, docking gently at its final destination. A refined, relatively quiet thrust engine propels the craft with surprising acceleration. Excellent receiver equipment monitors the many channels of Coruscant Air Traffic Control, allowing the pilot to use autonavigation or manual control at any time.

ABOVE AND BELOW

All significant traffic on Coruscant is air traffic—the original ground levels and roads having long ago been abandoned. Sealed tunnels in the lower realms allow for the transport of goods and materials through the city, as bulk shipments are barred by law from the crowded skylanes reserved for travelers.

EPISODE II
ATTACK OF THE CLONES

A decade has passed since the Trade Federation's blockade of Naboo. The unity of the galaxy is under threat as thousands of star systems break away from the Republic to join the Separatist movement, an organization led by the enigmatic Count Dooku. The Separatists' actions have made it difficult for the small number of Jedi Knights to maintain peace and order in the galaxy. After a divisive debate, the Senate passes the Military Creation Act, legitimizing the Republic's use of a clone army to counter the Separatist threat. Anakin Skywalker, now a Jedi Padawan, is apprenticed to Obi-Wan Kenobi, but Anakin's impatient nature is a source of much frustration to his Jedi mentor. Supreme Chancellor Palpatine takes an interest in Kenobi's apprentice, nurturing Anakin's growing dissatisfaction with the Jedi order. And as the galaxy teeters on the brink of war, the friendship between Anakin and Senator Padmé Amidala blossoms into a secret, forbidden love.

NABOO CRUISER

Few are surprised when Padmé Amidala descends from the throne of Naboo into the wider responsibilities of an appointment to the Senate. In fact, her esteem at the Naboo court remains so high that she continues to use a starship that features the highly distinctive chrome plating and sleek sculpting previously reserved exclusively for monarchs. Befitting one of the latest models from Theed Hangar, the Naboo cruiser is so finely polished that only the intentionally decorative seams remain visible. Though not armed itself, the cruiser travels with a guard convoy of starfighters.

Handmaidens' chamber

Seat for receiving petitions or chairing negotiations

Main access door with extensible ramp

Audience/ conference seating

Stasis-field horticapsule prolongs the fragile centennial bloom of Naboo bhansgrek bush

Forward portside sensor array

Power generator

Sensor preprocessors

Coolant pumps

Fuel lines

Hyper-pressurized fuel tanks

Fuel tank compressor bottles

Fighter recharge socket

Shield conduits and projector modules follow hull outlines

Portside repulsor antigrav generator

Post-reactor radiator

Coolant ducts connect to thermal sink

Thrust nozzle ring

Power feeds

Deflector shield projectors

Reaction chamber

Magnetic turbine

Electromagnetic thrust-vectoring vanes

Portside hyperdrive core

Cooling grid radiates waste heat to space

Thermal-sink matrix absorbs excess heat from reactors and thrusters

Portside-wing repulsor-array

Fighter recharge socket

LESSONS LEARNED

Naboo engineers corrected many of the drawbacks suffered by Padmé Amidala's Royal Starship during the infamous invasion of Naboo ten years earlier. The new ship is potently defensive, with a more-powerful shield generator, high-capacity energy-sink fins, and extensive projector units that efficiently circulate its protective force fields. The mass has been reduced and engine thrust doubled. Either of the two hyperdrives is singly capable of jumping the ship across lightspeed. In addition, the interior layout features increased space for conferences and greater separation of passengers and crew.

Galley

Life-support
air-scrubber

Condensed
oxygen
tanks

Pilot
stations

Comscan operator
and navigator
stations

Cooling shutter exposes
radiator and regulates
engine cooling

DARING ASSASSINATION

When a death-dealing explosion blows apart the cruiser as it lands on
Coruscant, Captain Typho assumes at first that a timed device must have been
hidden onboard the ship. However, a more complete investigation points to a
bomb on the landing platform itself having been remotely detonated. While
Padmé suspects Separatist scare-tactics, Typho privately fears that high-placed
insiders on Coruscant must have been involved for the tight security around the
Naboo delegation to be breached so successfully.

Turbolift to
cargo hold

Crew
lounge

Crew and
guard cabin

Crew locker

Bunk

Cables ground shield sinks
to general power network

Deadly Arrival Despite security precautions, Amidala's cruiser is
destroyed by a massive explosion moments after touching down on
a Coruscant landing pad.

Landing
gear
fairing

Hyperdrive-
navicomputer
control links

Main hold

Hyperdrive
maintenance
access hatch

Turbolift to
crew deck

Boarding
ramp

Cargo
cases

Maintenance
droids

Power
transmission
for shield
generator

Shield generator
maintenance access hatch

Deflector-shield generator
and ray-shield emitter

Shield-receiver heat sinks
and cooling radiators

Stern deflector
shield projectors

RELIABLE TRANSPORT

As a leading emissary, Padmé has relied on her graceful
diplomatic ship on scores of missions placating disgruntled
factions throughout her sector. Even in this sturdy vessel, however,
a thorough home constituency tour could last a lifetime in
Padmé's lightly populated Chommell Sector, which comprises 36
full-member worlds, more than 40,000 settled dependencies, and
300,000,000 barren stars. With more than 1,000 sectors, the
galaxy's deceptively fragile harmony depends on efficient divisions
of authority within the multi-tiered government, and upon the
wisdom of its roving officials and legislators.

Starfighter
docked in
recharge
socket

IN-FLIGHT SUPPORT

Hyperdrive-capable starfighters are naturally limited by fuel
capacity to jumps of less than 1,000 light-years. Previously,
Naboo N-1 fighters operating far from home could only travel in
small steps, accompanied by a tanker. After the invasion of
Naboo, designers added innovative recharge sockets to
the wings of the new diplomatic barge, thereby
enabling the ship to carry its own security
escort through hyperspace.

ZAM'S AIRSPEEDER

Hired assassin Zam Wesell flies an airspeeder that is as unusual and exotic as she is herself. The totally self-enclosed craft has no external thrusters and few air intakes because it was built for use on hostile, primitive worlds. Its repulsorlift units provide anti-gravity support, while other mechanisms generate radiation and electromagnetic fields that move the craft by dragging upon the air. This system is versatile enough for use in a huge variety of atmospheres. However, in urban areas, outdoor power lines can snag the propulsion fields and confound the steering— although this merely provides an extra means of traction to a cunning mercenary like Wesell.

WILDERNESS HARDWARE

The *Koro-2*'s forward mandibles operate as an external electromagnetic propulsion system. They intensely irradiate the air around them to induce ionization and make it conductive. Electrodes on each mandible project powerful electric currents across the gap, and the electrified air-stream is magnetically propelled toward the rear, thereby imparting thrust to the speeder. The speeder was designed for scouts exploring the wastelands of worlds lacking complex native life. Zam acquired hers on one of the billions of anonymous, young, highly-metalliferous planets dominated by the resource-hungry Mining Guild in the galaxy's spiral arms. Her use of it in downtrodden urban environments would dismay its designers.

Teraab Sector mining permit registration sticker

Radiators disperse waste heat and excess radioactivity

Heat exchanger

Starboard power generator

Streamlining reduces aerodynamic drag

Linear electric accelerators transmute inert gases

Transmuter cooling and refill vent

Generator insulation

Generator maintenance diagnostics

Bare seating and minimal head-rest

ASN-121 Assassin/ Sentry Droid

Doors swing upward

Luggage bin

Outer electrode surface naturally maintains its own sheen

Main radioactive gas delivery and containment shaft

Air dissociator radiation funnel

Prepared for a Getaway Standing on a Coruscant skyscraper's ledge, Zam Wesell takes aim at her target before she leaps into her waiting *Koro-2* airspeeder.

DIRTY TECHNOLOGY

Zam's speeder creates some hazardous side-effects that amuse the callous hunter. Irradiation zones are constrained around the mandibles, but can sicken unknowing innocent bystanders along the vehicle's path. Furthermore, drag-stream ions recombine chemically into unpleasant forms as they pass the cabin. In breathable atmospheres the products can include noxious gases that leave a foul reek in the speeder's wake.

Sinister Skills Her varied and dangerous career has made Wesell a very talented pilot, able to fly through the congested Coruscant skylanes at high speeds.

Variable air intake for generator cooling

Life-support systems

Steering yokes control repulsorlift balance for banking turns

Dashboard navigation controls

Status lights indicate cabin non-contamination

Control displays

Pedals control power to mandible propulsion systems

Fluorescent elements under translucent skin sense activity levels within operational ranges

Propulsion power systems, expanded upon standard model, protrude into mandible gap

Elongated storage bin for sniper rifle

Inner front surfaces have maximum piping density to provide the most intense irradiation

Maintenance log capsule

Inner electrode surface

Re-transmuter refreshes radioactivity during idle periods

Pump circulates radioactive fluid

Inner electrode anti-surge sink

Forward-scanner ranging device

Isolation shroud protects scanner

Power feeds to electromagnets

Propulsion system power cells

Superconducting electromagnet crystal elements

Vertical internal radiation shield

Irradiation gas distributor pipes

Shielded data cables connect instruments to cabin controls

Adaptive tuner regulates performance of right mandible propulsion systems

Forward power cells

SYMBOL OF EXTRAVAGANCE

The sophisticated and gaudy yellow airspeeder reflects the qualities of its youthful owner, Simon Greyshade, the newly risen Senator for the Vorzyd sector. The two-seat design fulfills Greyshade's desire for privacy while escorting fellow politicos, influential opinion-makers—or female companions. Its powerful communications gear helps keep Greyshade in contact with manipulators of galactic opinion. Clearly, this sly politician is beginning to enjoy the perks of office.

Communications gear

Racing stickers

Anakin uses his mechanical intuition to hotwire the speeder's security systems

Two-seat design

Tractor units in seats and inertial compensators keep occupants seated

Greyshade insists on sleek yellow styling for his personal craft

Anti-theft movement sensors (failed to detect Anakin's entry)

Exhaust thrust outlet

Yaw gyro casing

Generator diagnostics

Lateral repulsorlift array inside running-board

Pitch gyro casing and afterburner centrifuge

Powerful audio system

Lateral thrust-ducts distribute gas flow around cabin

Electro-gravitic gyro flywheels enable turning without relying on aerodynamics or ground traction

Thrust-duct attachment

Power generator

Deuterium fuel canisters

Gas-flow divertor tree

Force-diffusing chassis totally suppresses harmful engine vibrations

THRUST-DUCTS

The speeder is propelled through the air by a sophisticated system of thrust ducts. Highly over-pressured air flow from the turbojets is ignited and hurled through narrow thrust-ducts at transonic velocities. The main ducts pass through the cabin side walls. Secondary ducts are exposed on the speeder underbelly for cooling by air contact. Air streams pass through afterburner centrifuges and out of thrust vents at the back. The vents are partly covered by protective grilles, and have internal shutters to brake selectively or redirect the outflows.

ANAKIN'S AIRSPEEDER

When an attempt is made on the life of the Senator of Naboo and his Jedi Master is whisked off into the night air, Anakin Skywalker needs transport fast. With flawless intuition, he finds the perfect pursuit vehicle in the nearby senatorial parking zone. This overpowered, prized leisure craft, which belongs to a self-indulgent politician, is as quick and agile as any civilian airspeeder or cloud car in Coruscant's sky. Its complex and responsive system of repulsor units, thrust-ducting, and unconventional podracer-like engine arrangement provide one of the galaxy's best starpilots with the balance of superior control and instant familiarity essential for his daredevil pursuit of the assassin, Zam Wesell.

Left and right thrust-duct shutters and gyro turning are controlled by separate joysticks

Eight-speed thrust control/gear

Minimal windscreen forces the pilot to lean low in the seat

Electric field extends outside bonnet to repulse flying insects that would otherwise hit gleaming paintwork

Repulsor helps support weight of turbojet assembly

High Flier
The turbojets on Anakin's appropriated speeder burn brightly as he pursues an assassin across the skyscraper-choked skies of Coruscant.

Narrow-beam headlight

Turbine power cable

Left side engine bonnet

Turbofan and compression chamber

UNIQUE ENGINE LAYOUT
The powerful twin turbojet engines were designed for use in clusters of 50 in the wing nacelles of a colossal seventh-stage bank-courier repulsor-truck on Aargau. On this small speeder, they are overkill in power and expense. The unorthodox placement of the twin turbojet engines at the front of the speeder minimizes its width for good clearance in sky traffic or impromptu races through narrow urban mazes.

magnetic bottle regulators

Exposed turbojets flaunt the hotrod's brute power and reduce overheating

Ring of heavy-duty capacitors for turbofan drivers

Cold-start generator

Widebeam headlight and anti-collision scanner

Bumper made of exotic metal/condensed-matter composite spreads forces evenly and nearly instantly across entire chassis

Turbofan electromagnetic drivers and frictionless suspension

CORUSCANT SPEEDER CHASE

Covered entirely by densely packed skyscrapers, the planet Coruscant maintains a sophisticated global network of computers, sensors, and transmitters to ensure safety for millions of commuters, most of whom travel in droid-piloted vessels on designated aerial paths. However, Coruscant Air Traffic Control does allow Jedi and authorized law-enforcement officers to operate airspeeders relatively independently, enabling such pilots to veer out of the autonavigated skylanes to pursue and apprehend felons. When an assassin uses a droid to target Senator Amidala on Coruscant and flees in a waiting airspeeder, Obi-Wan Kenobi and Anakin Skywalker must chase her across Galactic City.

Repulsorlift array

Frontal tool-chuck

Fusion reactor core

Power converter array

Narrow shape minimizes target profile for enemies pursuing from behind or attacking from ahead

Cognitive central processor

Cooling vanes

Optical/infrared photoreceptor

Extendible cutter mandrel and kouhun canister dispenser

ASN-121—ASSASSIN/SENTRY DROID

Assassin Zam Wesell's ASN-121 droid is well-equipped for her deadly missions. Its frontal tool-chucks can wield a variety of implements and weapons, including a harpoon gun, sniper blaster, gas dispenser, spy sensors, flamethrower, and various drills and cutters. A compact fusion generator and modular power-converter array supply the rapidly varying energy demands of this dynamic machine, while independently powered repulsorlift rods work to ensure good balance even under unusual loads.

Maximum Velocity Seated behind the controls of a hastily appropriated airspeeder, Anakin ignores posted speed limits as he pursues an assassin's vehicle, and does little to assuage Obi-Wan's aversion to flying.

Custom-Made The height of the speeder's customized windscreen leaves the Jedi to assume the vehicle's owner is relatively short.

Holding on Tight After Anakin leaps onto the assassin's vehicle, the assassin swerves and dives in an effort to make the Jedi lose his grip.

FORCED LANDING

Although Coruscant Air Traffic Control's patrol officers, airborne droids, and extensive computer networks constantly monitor Coruscant's skylanes, they can't chase down every airspeeder that breaks away from designated routes, or prevent every shuttle with a damaged repulsorlift engine from crashing. Fortunately, if a Jedi witnesses dangerous or illegal activity in the skylanes, they are fully authorized to intervene. As a result, in an effort to stop an assassin from escaping in a *Koro-2* all-environment exodrive speeder, Anakin Skywalker is compelled to do everything in his power to stop the vehicle. Incredibly, the speeder crashes on one of the lower-level thoroughfares in the Uscru Entertainment District without killing any civilians.

Jedi Intervention Anakin not only manages to cling to the assassin's speeder, but also activates his lightsaber and plunges it into the cockpit.

Crash Site Given the great efficiency of Coruscant Air Traffic Control, a crashed airspeeder is a rare sight on low-level pedestrian walkways.

JEDI STARFIGHTER

When Obi-Wan Kenobi departs on his quest to Kamino, he requisitions one of the Jedi Temple's modified Delta-7 *Aethersprite* light interceptors. This ultra-light fighter is well shielded against impacts and blasts, and is equipped with two dual laser cannons that can unleash a withering frontal assault. Its sleek, blade-like form simplifies shield distribution and affords excellent visibility, especially in forward and lateral directions. A fighter of this size normally cannot travel far into deep space on its own, but the customized Jedi version features a socket for a truncated droid navigator and can dock with an external hyperdrive ring. Its offensively-focused design assumes dominance over any foe—essential for a prescient Jedi or any steely-nerved pilot trained for frontal assaults.

ANCIENT ICON

The starboard wing of Obi-Wan's craft is marked with the symbol of a disc with eight spokes. This ancient icon dates to the Bendu monks' study of numerology, whereby the number nine (eight spokes joined to one disc) signifies the beneficent presence of the Force in a unitary galaxy. After the fall of the Galactic Republic 1,000 generations later, the Emperor will personalize this symbol by defacing the icon with the removal of two spokes.

External Hyperdrive
Because the Delta-7 does not have a built-in hyperdrive, Obi-Wan utilizes a hyperdrive ring to travel through hyperspace. After he reaches his destination, the Delta-7 detaches from the ring, which remains in orbit until it is needed again.

STOICAL DROID

Originally an R4-series astromech droid, R4-P17 was crushed while repairing trash compactor faults in the KDY research shipyards over Gyndine. While inspecting the Jedi customizations of the Delta-7 design, Anakin Skywalker found R4's wreck and rebuilt her with an R2-series dome. Now Temple property, R4 is the prototype for other integrated droid navigators in Jedi Delta-7 ships.

The fighter's tiny profile makes it difficult to detect and easy to hide from long-range sensors

Ancient roundel with eight spokes

Red coloration indicates Jedi plenipotentiary status and diplomatic immunity

Deflector shield power hub

Transformers and power cells for bow hardware

Firing groove

Power feeds to bow deflectors

Forward landing gear bay

Port landing light

Forward deflector shield projectors

Main reactor bulb

Laser cannon capacitors

Forward ventral power tree

Dual laser cannon emitter muzzles

Comscan processor

Communications and scanning reflector dish

Multi-mode scanning and communications transceiver

Landing pad is a descending hull panel

Ventral landing claw enables docking in zero-gravity environments, such as on planetary ring boulders

PRIVILEGED NETWORK SCOUT

In an emergency, Kenobi's ship can relay encrypted signals via any suitably powerful hyperwave transceiver located in the same planetary system. During the mission to Geonosis, Obi-Wan uses a powerful interstellar relay station in the Geonosis system to communicate with Anakin on Tatooine.

Monastic Attire
On this mission, Obi-Wan opts against wearing the sealable, semi-armored spacesuit available to Jedi for space flight, in favor of a meditative robe.

Cockpit canopy

Heat-sink and radiator for energy absorbed by shield

Seat restraints

Shield generator

Reactant tank

Flight instruments

Aft shield projectors

Atmospheric life support

Electromagnetic nozzle elements direct and pinch the relativistic thrust steam

Landing gear bay

Foot step

Engine cooling duct outlet

Laser cannon maintenance panel

Repulsor vanes infused with micro-coils of gravitic knots

R4-P17 manages hyperspace navigation, as well as the fighter's supplementary scanning and communications gear

Heat shield

Thermal discharge vent for waste mesons

Power convertor

Tibanna coolant gas hose

Resonator shaft

Beam splitter

FORETASTE OF SUCCESS

Tariff barriers and embargoes between the galaxy's sectors prevent direct competition between Kuat Drive Yards, Republic Sienar Systems, Incom, and other military shipbuilders. In years to come, Kuat will gain a near monopoly on warship contracts for Palpatine's centralized fleet, although rival Sienar will win most government business for starfighters. Thus the technically excellent Delta-7 starfighter will be extinct in ten years, while its kilometers-long cousins, the Star Destroyers, will continue to fill KDY's bountiful catalog.

JEDI STARSHIPS

While the Jedi Order typically uses Republic cruisers for diplomatic missions across the galaxy, some assignments require smaller and less conspicuous transports. And because Jedi can't always rely on pilots to reach their destination, Jedi training includes how to fly starships. The Jedi Temple on Coruscant contains hangars for numerous vessels, including single-passenger starfighters. Although most Jedi starfighters are engineered to accommodate humanoid Jedi, some are designed for specific alien species.

In-Flight Support Engineered without a traditional built-in navicomputer, the Delta-7 *Aethersprite* Jedi starfighter utilizes a truncated astromech droid.

Evasive Maneuvers Obi-Wan Kenobi guides his Jedi starfighter through an asteroid belt in a daring effort to evade an enemy missile.

"Blast! This is why I hate flying."
Obi-Wan Kenobi

JEDI TRACER BEACONS
A miniature tracking device, tracer beacons are sophisticated transmitters used to follow starships and pinpoint their exact location. Some tracer beacons, such as the one Obi-Wan Kenobi uses to track Jango Fett's *Slave I,* are magnetic to lock onto a ship's hull, and can even track a ship's journey through hyperspace.

Magnetic Landing Claw The Delta-7 *Aethersprite* light interceptor is equipped with a ventral landing claw, a magnetic gripping device that can adhere to almost any surface, including rocky asteroids.

WEAPON OF A BOUNTY HUNTER

Kuat Drive Yard's *Firespray* patrol craft saw only limited production, as it was too heavily armed for civilian use yet was underpowered by Kuat's home-defense standards. Furthermore, *Firesprays* proved too robust, modular, and user-serviceable to support a profitable post-sale maintenance business. Although bad for the manufacturer, these characteristics make it a perfect starship for an independent bounty hunter like Jango Fett.

Sensor Scopes *Slave I*'s sensor scopes display readouts for weapons systems as well as navigational and atmospheric data.

INTERIOR REFIT

Originally stolen by Jango on the asteroid prison Oovo 4, *Slave I* has been extensively modified after a few harsh space battles. Jango has added spartan crew quarters for long hunts, since the original *Firespray* was furnished for shorter-term patrols. In addition, the police-regulation prisoner cages have been converted into less-humane, coffin-like wall cabinets to ensure control of captives.

On the Attack Piloting *Slave I* past hazardous asteroids, Jango Fett opens fire on a Jedi starfighter that has followed him from Kamino to Geonosis.

DEVASTATING ASSETS

Slave I's tail blaster cannons are the only overt weaponry retained from the standard *Firespray*, but they have been enhanced with finer aim and variable power. Rapid-fire laser cannons concealed amidships have less control than the tail guns, but deliver kiloton-scale energy bolts at a greater rate. Fett has installed physical armaments as well: an adapted naval minelayer deals nasty surprises to hasty pursuers, and a concealed, frontal double-rack of torpedoes fulfils the role of a guided, heavy-assault weapon.

Slave I Originally one of several prototype patrol ships made by Kuat Systems Engineering, *Slave I* is an extremely rare and distinctively designed starship.

JANGO FETT'S SLAVE I

Jango Fett pilots a viciously effective, customized starship with superior shielding combined with high endurance levels, and a heavy arsenal of overt and hidden weapons. At first glance, the rugged vessel is recognizable as an ordinary *Firespray*-class law-enforcement patrol ship. However, closer inspection reveals a montage of patched, rebuilt, and enhanced equipment attesting to its unsavory usage. Jango favors this uncommon but unexotic craft for the element of disguise it affords him; as one of the galaxy's most proficient mercenaries, he nonetheless chooses to work in discreet obscurity, remaining unrecognized by most highly placed security officers and criminals alike. When Jango's son Boba inherits *Slave I*, he will make some changes to suit his greater infamy and more aggressive style, including increased interstellar range and fuel capacity, installation of superior sensor jammers, and other stealth hardware.

Bounty Hunter's Landing Pad The Kaminoans designated a Tipoca City landing platform for Jango Fett's personal use. Accustomed to rapid escapes, Jango makes sure *Slave I* is always prepared for immediate departure.

Energy-shield shroud

Ladder to lower level

Corridor segment scavenged from a derelict Corellian starliner

Fins contain repulsor grilles for landing maneuvers

Jango Fett

Boba Fett

Each deck's artificial gravity re-orients depending on flight mode

Flight instruments

Expansion grid for future hardware (Boba will install stealth gear)

Upper portside inertial compensator

Sublight communications antenna

Shield generator main power conduit

Forward shield generator destined for relocation to make room for larger power cells and fuel tanks

Jango's bunk

Forward starboard reactant tank

Guard console

Entry hatch inner doors

Scanner tubes

Disintegrator chute atomizes waste

Manhole hatch

Maintenance crawlspace ladder

Static discharge vent

Target scanner

Adaptive sensor-targeting processor and power regulator

Twin blaster cannons with 360° rotation and 10° range of tilt

Modified concussion missile inflicts blast-like kinetic effects without physical contact

Missile launcher

Missile launcher under concealed panel

Engineering console

Hidden laser cannon fires two-kiloton-yield energy bolts (Boba will later replace it with an ion cannon)

Makeshift external power lines feed tail cannons from a non-standard generator and capacitor array

Cover retracts from concealed weapon

Enhanced Cannons
Jango Fett upgraded *Slave I*'s original blaster cannons so they can be fired with greater precision as well as power in planetary atmospheres or interstellar vacuum.

Wing articulation

Yellow light indicates that mine is primed

Minelayer magazine

Thruster nozzle

Ion drive pre-accelerator

Power generator

Hull attachment grounds ion drive

Engine systems waste heat pump and sink

Radiator fins

Handle opens
sliding drawer
of pannier

Cooler
compartment lid

Water
bottles

Food storage (includes
crimplecress slices and
roasted duodecipede
(leg sticks)

Lock-down lid handle

Thermally insulated casing

Straps secure luggage

FANCY FLYING

Swoops handle in ways that confound many novices. Steering
vanes may have less influence on turning and speed than the
weight and air resistance of the rider. Variable repulsorlift
forces must also be understood: total output determines lift
force, but its spread across the repulsor array affects balance.

Tarpaulin to cover large
loads, or act as
emergency shelter

Upper lid
fastener
strap

Rail on which
pannier interior
slides out

Bag of heads
for multi-tool

Portable
scanner

Versatile
multi-tool

Comlink

Seat cushion

Mask and
goggles for use
in sandstorms

Blaster for defense

Emergency
power pack

Reel for fishing
edible spiky shelled
duodecipedes
out of their burrows

Pannier
mount
frame

Rear steering
vanes

Homing beacon/
geopositioner

HARSH TERRITORY

Tatooine's searing climate is far removed from the
common image of armchair farming in hydroponic
shells around prestigious agri-industrial worlds like
Fengrine. Owen's days are spent riding his swoop
across a merciless suns-bleached land, tending to
distant moisture vaporators, uprooting tenacious
pests and checking faults in perimeter shields that
deter roaming predators and Tusken Raider assaults.

Replaceable generator
core rod

Power
generator

Generator settings
switches

Generator vent

Jet pipe
heat shield

Ventral fins

Fuel
filler

Antigrav
generate

Cable shroud

Pressure-activated
accelerator pedal

Seven-stage
compressor

Combustion chamber

Jet exhaust and
thrust pipe

PRACTICAL MOBILITY

Affordable air-taxis, comfortable limousine speeders, reliable public air
buses, and speeder trams meet most needs on urbanized planets. However,
on underdeveloped backwater worlds, owning a private vehicle is a vital
aspect of personal independence for people of all classes and professions.
In the remote deserts of lawless Tatooine, farming youngsters like Owen
Lars fly and repair swoops and speeders from childhood. Under the guise of
helping out with the daily chores, many bored young people on lonely
moisture farms seek much-needed excitement by driving the family
vehicle, often at breakneck speeds.

Igniter

Rear impeller

High-pressure
fuel lines

OWEN LARS'S SWOOP BIKE

Of all people on desolate Tatooine, the implacable moisture farmers have the most pragmatic appreciation of vehicular technology, upon which they depend for daily survival. Young Owen Lars epitomizes this principle, as he patrols the family property on his fast, sand-beaten swoop. Though not especially reliable, this farm vehicle is used more heavily than the homestead's dozen other semi-restored craft because it is fuel-efficient and easy to repair using Jawa-supplied parts. Owen bought his high-powered swoop from a Revwien merchant at an auction in remote Mos Nytram. Originally a racing vehicle, he immediately saw its practical use. Townsfolk might scoff at the sight of a one-time sports vehicle hauling water trailers or vermin traps, but as far as Owen is concerned, utility is the true essence of grace.

Setting adjusts spread of repulsor field

Compressor spin clutch

Fuel gauges

Fuel cock

Control wire trunk

Tank partition

Setting adjusts repulsorlift force

Airscoop shutter brake

Airscoop shutter lift and tilt switch

Steering vanes exert turning forces against airflow far from the scoop's center of mass

Two reactants in separate fuel tanks

Steering vane twisting joints

Steering vane actuation/ support forks

Shutter regulates air intake

Fuel lines

Repulsorlift array

Resident leebsie-lurker eats insects splattered in the grille and filters

Frontal sand-grille

Airscoop

Fuel lines

Control cables

Holding pin

Dust electro-filter elements

Fuel mixing chamber

Front impeller

Desperate Hunt After learning that his mother was abducted by Tusken Raiders on Tatooine, Anakin Skywalker borrows Owen Lars's swoop bike and follows the trail of the murderous Sand People.

LATEST MODEL

Owen's swoop is regarded as one of the latest styles on the backwater planet of Tatooine, although it slid off an assembly line at least 20 years before his birth. Indeed, this model—and ones like it—had been in common use many years earlier on richer, more central worlds. Down the ages, technological fashions spread incredibly slowly through the galaxy's millions of inhabited systems, even though the actual technology generally fluctuates only in scale and implementation.

SWOOP ENGINE

In its functional simplicity, the swoop is a tube. At the front, an airscoop feeds a turbojet in which fuel is mixed and ignited. At the rear, a tail-piped exhaust stream provides thrust. A repulsor array under the seat keeps the bike aloft, and is sustained by basic power cells and a generator. The only moving parts are the fans and gears of the compressor. These mechanisms are protected from abrasive sand and dust by a coarse grille at the airscoop mouth, followed by multiple electrostatic filters.

PADMÉ'S STARSHIP

This slim yacht from the royal hangars of Naboo is not a spacious diplomatic platform for long-range tours and conferences. It is a relatively fast ship suited to discreet getaways. Its security features include a powerful Naboo-style shield system, electronic countermeasures, and a last-resort passenger escape capsule. Queen Jamillia's royal starships normally sit idle since she prefers to concentrate on Naboo's domestic affairs, entrusting her external powers to Senator Padmé Amidala. The smallest royal yacht is therefore available and ideally suited for Padmé's undercover travels as the galaxy's most threatened political target. The yacht serves Padmé and Anakin well in their dangerous journey from Tatooine to the neighboring Geonosis system.

Coolant pump circulates a superfluid with enormous heat capacity to moderate the shield matrix during critical power spikes that cannot be radiated away quickly

Gleaming hull plating acts as passive physical radiation shielding

Deflector shield projector modules

Shield heat-sink and radiator matrix

Shield generator

Navicomputer housing and power trunk

Tube containing turbolift platform connects upper and lower deck for fast access

Navigator station

Anakin

Anakin's crew bunk

Auxiliary comscan station

Toolkit

Ship's manual

Main reactor

Galley

Orderly and aesthetically arranged Naboo circuitry

Astromech droid hold (two stations)

Connection to main reactor above

Starboard antigrav generator

Power node

Power trunk starboard fork

INCONSPICUOUS TRANSPORT

The yacht is the smallest non-fighter vessel kept in the hangars of Theed Palace. Its simplified systems reduce maintenance time, making it ideal for secretive, unsupported excursions. It is much faster than most civilian ships, and its narrow profile and sheltered engines create only a small sensor signature. Its small crew requirements also minimize the risk of sabotage, allowing Padmé and Anakin to pilot the ship alone, with back-up assistance from the droids C-3PO and R2-D2.

Starboard stern repulsor coils

Extended boarding ramp

Reactor fuel tank

Fuel baffles

Stores

Airlock

Hull substrate

R2-D2's station (unused)

Slim, aerodynamic shape facilitates unshielded hypersonic flight in atmosphere

Bow forward scanners

Communications array

Padmé runs the initial preflight check

Pilot station

RESPECTED NABERRIE

Upon her return to Naboo, Padmé seeks the security of close friends and allies in the district of her birth. Here, as on Coruscant, she is addressed as "M'lady," instead of "Senator," as protocol dictates given her years of service as Naboo's elected queen. When she spontaneously decides to accompany Anakin to Tatooine, the Naboo authorities are ready to trust Padmé's instincts and commandeer a royal starship for her use.

Forward dorsal power spine

Emergency aerial

Forward maintenance crawlway

Emergency particle-flare launcher

Explosive bolts fill gap between capsule and hull

Traditional Naboo handcrafted bed

Throne/bedfoot

Bright floor marks denote hardpoints and bulkheads

Main power spine passes through hyperdrive core

C-3PO

Propulsion systems maintenance console

Hyperdrive core

Ionization chamber

R2-D2

Flank deflector shield projectors

Complex magnetic ducts guide ion stream past intruding landing gear housing

Landing gear

Sublight drive particle exit ring

Starboard inertial compensator

Beru Whitesun

Owen Lars

STEALTHY APPROACH

When nearing and landing on Geonosis, Padmé and Anakin lower the yacht's shield power to reduce easily detectible energy by-product emissions. An unshielded or lightly shielded ship passively hurtling down into a planet's atmosphere might be mistaken for a meteorite, and, since Geonosis is surrounded by a rocky planetary ring, Anakin guesses correctly that its scanner technicians are lazy about meteor-like detections.

Communications Console During their mission to Tatooine, Padmé Amidala and Anakin Skywalker are on the Nubian yacht's bridge when they receive a holographic transmission from Jedi Master Mace Windu on Coruscant.

SECURITY SENSITIVITY

The Trade Federation occupation significantly changed Naboo defense policy, with increased harmony between Naboo and Gungans resulting in coordinated action plans to withstand any new siege. Gungan shield expertise was combined with Naboo power generation to form a global shield network that activates in minutes to repel any bombardment or hostile landing. The need for such effective, if discreet, homeworld defenses is popularly supported. Captain Panaka's Security Forces have a healthy supply of volunteers, and Theed Palace engineers are designing a steady series of new starships to convey their dignitaries.

TRADE FEDERATION CORE SHIP

With its fleets of freighter-battleships, the Neimoidian Trade Federation is well-equipped to be one of the powerful merchant factions behind the advent of the Clone Wars. The heart and brain of each battleship is a detachable Core Ship, which comprises a massive central computer and multiple power systems. These huge ships are serviced in special landing pits on planets affiliated to the Trade Federation, while the delicate cargo arms and engine blocks remain in orbit. The Core Ships' ion-drive nozzles provide basic steering and slow acceleration, allowing them to dock in powerful anti-gravity repulsorlift cushions, with eight landing legs for stability. Scores of these ships are grounded on Geonosis, where they are being upgraded for coordination with the newly enhanced Baktoid droid armies. During the battle on Geonosis, the Core Ships are ringed with land and air defenses, allowing a good number to retreat safely to the skies.

VERTICAL ORGANIZATION

The hierarchical arrangement of habitable areas on a Core Ship matches that of Neimoidian hives. The control bridges, executive suites, and treasuries are concentrated in the globe's upper pole and towers, and resemble Neimoidia's luxurious surface palaces. Deeper levels are for junior managers, publicists, brokers, and droid storage. The lowest decks contain engineering areas and conference rooms for meeting outsiders; like the unfavorably dry and hot basements of Neimoidian warrens, frequented by subterranean scavengers and parasites, these decks are shunned by high-ranking officials.

Massive Evacuation After the Republic's newly formed army arrives on Geonosis, the Neimoidians flee to their Trade Federation Core Ships. Extremely powerful repulsorlift engines enable the enormous ships to achieve escape velocity.

STANDARD PART

Core-Ship design has changed little in the last century. In a typical display of Neimoidian thrift, the spheres can serve a variety of craft: The split-ring freighter-battleships of the Naboo blockade; larger, unarmed container vessels and tankers; and newer warships of the post-Naboo period, including cruisers with improved weapons placement and smaller, faster destroyers that defend the fleets and chase down blockade runners.

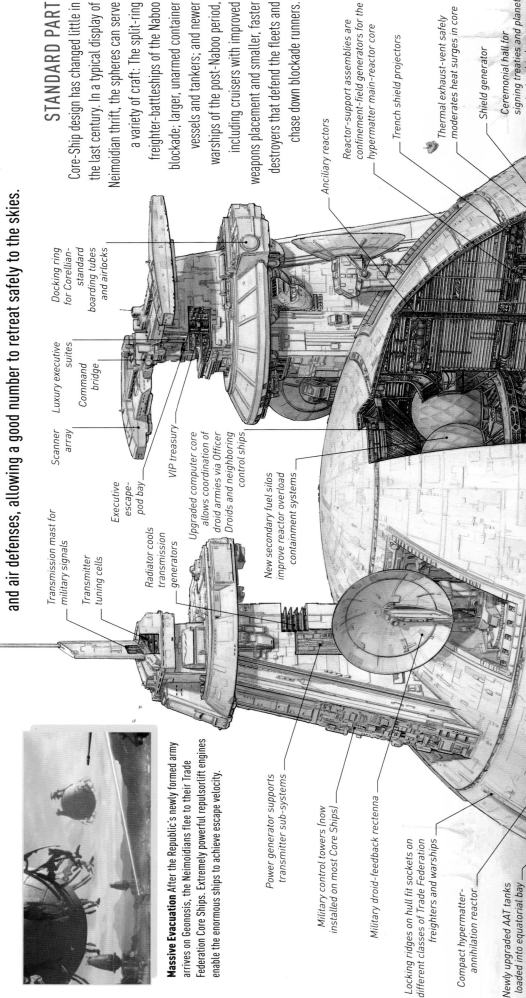

Anciliary reactors

Reactor-support assemblies are confinement-field generators for the hypermatter main-reactor core

Trench shield projectors

Thermal exhaust-vent safely moderates heat surges in core

Shield generator

Ceremonial hall for signing treaties and planetary

Docking ring for Corellian-standard boarding tubes and airlocks

Luxury executive suites

Command bridge

Scanner array

VIP treasury

Executive escape-pod bay

Upgraded computer core allows coordination of droid armies via Officer Droids and neighboring control ships

New secondary fuel silos improve reactor overload containment systems

Transmission mast for military signals

Transmitter tuning cells

Radiator cools transmission generators

Power generator supports transmitter sub-systems

Military control towers (now installed on most Core Ships)

Military droid-feedback rectenna

Locking ridges on hull fit sockets on different classes of Trade Federation freighters and warships

Compact hypermatter-annihilation reactor

Newly upgraded AAT tanks loaded into equatorial bay

uninhabited but patrolled by security droids

C-9979 landing ship parts

Droid battalions

Boarding ramp

New storage holds added after full militarization

Heavy cargo lift

Retractable maintenance gantry

Power feeds recharge ship systems

Landing gear retractors

Faster-than-light "hyperwave" transceiver reaches any part of the galaxy directly without use of public HoloNet relays

Hull sections from leg socket cover

Foot-pads

Anti-gravity repulsorlift suspensors

NEW ALLY

After more than a decade of promoting its own trade interests by underhand means, the Trade Federation recognizes the strategic value of Count Dooku. As a persuasive orator with a zealous following on thousands of Separatist worlds, including Geonosis (home to the Federation's favorite dockyards and armorers), he is fostering disunity throughout the galaxy—and, as Nute Gunray knows, weak governments are good for business.

Ventral thruster extends out of a lower hatch

Rings project one-way force-field that confines harmful radiation from the ship's exhaust in the blast shaft

HYPERLANE CONTROL

Core Ships' navicomputers contain precious interstellar data charts. In bygone ages, governments and private agencies shared such information publicly, but now the Trade Federation aggressively protects the coordinates it owns. As changes in astronomical conditions can make routes unsafe, the Trade Federation is gaining a virtual transport monopoly over parts of the galaxy. Now, only the Jedi and the Office of the Supreme Chancellor can afford to maintain more comprehensive charts.

Defensive artillery

Waste fluid vent

Artillery power generator

Observation stations and workshops

Lift shaft

Walls are lined with gravitational reflectors for the ship's repulsors to act against

Particle shields cycle and intensify in trenches

Small, point-defense turrets

Thruster blast and radiation are harmlessly channeled into shaft

GEONOSIAN FIGHTER

During the climactic battle with the Republic, the Geonosian faction launches thousands of standby fighters to break the Republic's orbital cordon blocking Corporate Alliance ground reinforcements. These fightercraft combine high linear acceleration with phenomenal maneuverability as a result of the frictionless rotating mount of their thrusters. Despite their superior agility, few fighters are exported, since Geonosian senses and articulation differ from the galaxy's majority humanoid population. Furthermore, Geonosian policy has become fervently isolationist as the Republic stagnates, and their wary Archduke, Poggle the Lesser, believes that the hoarding of technical advantages is an insurance of power and security.

FLYING BY NOSE

An advanced scent stimulator in the pilot's mask exploits the acute Geonosian sense of smell to convey flight status feedback. The mask also sprays subverbal pheromone signals so that air marshals and flight controllers can remotely modify the pilot's mood and impart collective priorities.

Geonosian dexterity needed to operate complex multi-axis control yokes

Visual readouts for fire control and spatial orientation

Pilot's scent-stimulator mask

Laser cannon trigger

Propellant regulator

Endostructural frame

Communications transceivers

Flight computer

Propellant tank cluster

Flexible propellant hose maintains connection as engine ball rotates

Propellant is excited into high-energy subatomic particles in the ignition chamber

Power cables to cannon suspensors and inductors

Landing gear actuators

Bottle field permits only the highest velocity particles to shine out in collimated thrust beams

Engine orb rotates in socket

Superconducting magnetic suspensors

Starboard scanners

Main reactor refuel and recharge pads

Low-maintenance main reactor fills almost entire rear of lower hull

Power converter

Landing gear surface panel

Self-contained gun-turret orb

Laser cannon yaw traverse track

FLEXIBLE FRAMEWORK

Geonosian starship frames are built from long strings of laminasteel, which can be woven and wrapped at high temperatures, binding together the ship's components. The frame cools to a metallic hardness, yet the bonds can momentarily yield and rebound enough to survive impacts that would break a more rigidly constituted vessel.

Deadly Escorts After Dooku orders his protecting fighters to attack a pursuing Republic gunship, the agile vessels maneuver behind it and open fire. The gunship is destroyed, but its Jedi passengers survive.

Covers are permeable to shield and tractor projections

Ventral prong power trunk

Forward inertial compensator sub-node

Tractor and shield kickback dampers

Bronze cladding is an austere and inconspicuous hue on the reddish-brown planet Geonosis

Long barrel of laser cannon imparts greater spin to the emergent beam and reduces collateral bolt glow relative to destructive power

MODULAR ORBS

One of the most distinctive design features of the Geonosian Fighter are its gun turret and engine orbs. These are magnetically suspended and inductively powered without direct contact. The sockets fit many alternative modules such as engine boosters and enhanced scanner suites for surveillance missions.

Grapple notches for docking clamp

Laser cannon fires along the neutral space in between the prong shields

Recoil brackets cushion cannon during outburst of its own waste gases

Green highlights resemble markings on the pygmy porlceetin—a large, venomous, hexapedal creature found on Geonosis

As gun-turret orb rolls, different power-induction spots overlap fixed points on socket wall

Dooku's Speeder Bike On Geonosis, Count Dooku escapes the Republic forces using a Flitknot speeder bike manufactured by Huppla Pasa Tisc, a Geonosian corporation. Dooku's speeder bike has been modified to suit his personal and physical requirements, and a pair of Geonosian fighters serve as Dooku's escorts.

GEONOSIAN TECHNOLOGY

Natives of the Outer Rim planet Geonosis, Geonosians are quasi-insectoids who developed and perfected technology for precision droid manufacturing in bulk. For centuries, they dedicated their hive-based culture to the production of protocol, labor, and combat droids in alliance with the Techno Union's Baktoid Corporation. The Geonosians were responsible for hundreds of thousands of battle droids used during the Battle of Naboo. Their sprawling subterranean complexes contain not only numerous droid factories, but research and development laboratories for exotic vehicles and experimental weapons.

Geonosis Hangar Not far from the Geonosian Command Center, a hangar holds a waiting shuttle for the Neimoidian dignitaries, two Geonosian fighters, and Count Dooku's speeder bike.

HIVE PILOTS

As well as being masters of Battle Droid design, the Geonosians raise a caste of living combat pilots in immense cob-shaped air-defence hives. Pilots can potentially spend years poised for action, as their hardy species requires no sleep. In training, each pilot pupa pairs with a fighter's flight computer, and they develop an idiosyncratic, coordination-enhancing rapport.

Cockpit hatch opens for technical servicing and cleaning or repairing a pilot

Diagnostics console

Propellant refuelling conjugator

Cockpit hinge

Pilot stairs

Rear hull shield generator

Integrated shield and tractor beam projectors

Dorsal frame spine

Intermediary power cell

Forward dorsal scanner lines

Shoulder joint for release of docking clamp

Recharge cabling

Laser cannon

Dorsal capacitor distributes power throughout upper prong

Blaster coolant gas refiller hose (disengaged)

Docking clamp

Main inertial compensator and internal gravity generator

Holographic Command Table At the center of the Geonosian Command Center, a large circular table displays holograms of the ongoing battle on Geonosis between Republic and Separatist forces.

Death Star Designs Although the concept of a moon-sized superweapon originated with the Republic engineer Raith Sienar, the initial plans were secretly passed to the Geonosians, who helped devise the weapon's hypermatter systems.

REPUBLIC ASSAULT FORCES

Mere days after Obi-Wan Kenobi discovers the existence of a clone army allegedly commissioned for the Republic by a since-deceased Jedi, members of the Galactic Senate agree to conscript the army to fight the Separatists. Although the clones have received extensive training on Kamino, none of them has experienced actual combat before arriving on Geonosis. Jedi Masters Yoda and Mace Windu both lead full battle armies, while other veteran Jedi Knights each lead over 36,000 troops.

Command Center Stationed on an air-dropped mobile command center, clone officers and technicians monitor troop positions, enemy movements, communications, and sensor data to assist their comrades and Jedi generals.

SPHA-T Self-Propelled Heavy Artillery-Turbolasers (SPHA-Ts) are deployed in squads of four behind advancing Republic walkers, providing defense for landing assault ships, and destructive direct firepower.

HEAVY ARTILLERY

Just as the Galactic Senate was quick to utilize the clone army without investigating the army's mysterious origin, the Republic readily embraced a ready-made armada of weapons and heavily armed vessels and vehicles. Most of the Galactic Army's arsenal was manufactured by Rothana Heavy Engineering, a subsidiary of Kuat Drive Yards, a corporation that had been opposed to the Separatists for years. The arsenal includes assault ships, transports, bombers, and combat airspeeders. Clone soldiers, all having trained with exotic weapons simulators, have no difficulty operating actual weapons of war.

Combined Arms Equipped with laser cannons and missile launchers, assault gunships rain fire on enemy vehicles as they deliver clone troopers to the battlefront.

COMPOSITE BEAM TURRETS

The wing- and armature-mounted ball turrets enjoy a wide field of rotation in order to strike targets both above and below the horizontal plane. They are intended for defense against airborne hostiles. The merger of precisely synchronized tributary beams confers pinpoint aiming precision far beyond that of the turret's physical rotation.

Ready for Flight Clone gunship pilots received intensive training on Kamino via flight simulators, giving them greater flight skills than most veteran pilots.

Generator

Transformer distributes power to subsystems

Co-pilot/ gunner

Pilot

Flight computer

Navigational terrain-sensor housing

Computer interface ports for servicing in hangar

Power feeds to front laser cannons

Laser cannon power feed access panel

Light indicates atmospheric integrity of front sections

Airtight hatch to front compartments

Handhold

Armature swings turret in or out of main hold

Deckplates give access to main repulsor array

Protruding deck ledge gives deploying troops a clear view

Insulated armored sheath guides belt frictionlessly

Blaster cratering on superficial armor

Ball turret traverses its socket freely and elevates to the limits of its firing dishes

Variable output of wingtip repulsor grille affects roll of gunship

Turret suspension rollers, magnetic clamps, and power-feed modules

Remote-controlled firing dishes allow both dorsal and ventral coverage

Air-to-air rockets

Firing dish exploits non-superposition of blaster energy to compose variable tributary beams into a finely aimed, intense composite beam

Turret elevation guides

Side door swings back and outward

Open viewports double as sockets for docking clamps in maintenance hangars

TACTICAL ADVANTAGE

These strategic transport craft and their variants are maneuverable enough to fly low and exploit the natural cover of Geonosis' precipitous ravines and spires. Their long mass driver barrels can accelerate projectiles up to hypersonic velocities. Once launched, missiles engage self-powered flight along either a programmed trajectory or following encrypted guidance signals. Telemetry (remote communication) comes from either an orbiting mothership or signals routed from ground units within sight of the target, including advance scout troops.

Side-door support-arm ejects explosively in the event of a crash

SURVIVAL AND RECOVERY

Each fully trained clone soldier represents a considerable investment, so crew have several escape options when their gunship is disabled. In the worst survivable scenarios, the entire cockpit section ejects as an escape capsule. After a failed landing, the cockpit canopies can be blown off. If the exit is blocked below the cockpits, crew use external climbing steps built into the hull. Injured or isolated men are retrieved whenever possible. The LAAT/i repulsorlift gunship is their primary recovery vehicle. Emergency equipment in forward lockers includes a globular IM-6 Battlefield Medical Droid, medical packs, armor repair kits, collapsible repulsor stretchers, and inflatable decontamination tents.

DIVERSE ORDNANCE

The LAAT gunship's use of missiles and energy weapons provides complementary benefits. Whereas a blaster can almost instantly hit anything within a clear line of sight, a missile may go around obstacles and over the horizon. Conversely, while a missile can sometimes be dodged or shot down, an energy beam cannot be intercepted, except by shield absorption. Missile payloads are variable and mission-specific, including simple omnidirectional blasts, corrosive antimatter showers, electromagnetic pulse effects, sterilizing bursts of hard radiation, or concentrated thermal effects.

Missile belts thread between engines

Heavy cladding around initial boost chamber

Superficial burns from exhaust of launching missiles

Heat-sink and radiator

Internal shock absorbers

Exhaust slats can tilt to direct thrust streams

Damaged starboard engine is on fire internally

Rocket back-blast vent

Tail repulsor and engine diagnostics

ail cannon defends troops r scout vehicles exiting rough stern hatch

Fuel tank

Speeder bike's power cells and thrust exhaust

Speeder bike seat

Speeder bike's turbojet airscoop

Steering vanes

Chain moves missile belt

Burning wreckage

REPUBLIC GUNSHIP

The Galactic Republic's LAAT/i (Low-Altitude Assault Transport/infantry) aerial gunships play a vital role in the battle on Geonosis. These tactical transport craft and their variants can fly over impassibly rough terrain to swiftly and safely disgorge an entire platoon of clone troopers, or haul a slower armored vehicle into position. Enemy fighters must either remain at high altitudes or surrender their speed advantage when pursuing gunships below the mountain level. A Republic assault ship's entire gunship complement can deliver more than 2,000 soldiers in each wave. However, these flying troop carriers are versatile gun platforms in their own right, too. They are lighter and faster than mobile artillery and most ground vehicles, yet still carry a considerable arsenal. Massive twin missile launchers allow concerted over-the-horizon strikes on slow or fixed targets, such as enemy artillery and fortifications. Two pairs of widely rotating blaster cannons defend the gunship with deadly precision. Finally, three chin- and tail-mounted laser cannons devastate enemy infantry and other light ground assets.

Power feeds to wing repulsors and turret

REPUBLIC ASSAULT SHIP

The arrival of massive *Acclamator*-class troopships above Geonosis is a pivotal moment in galactic military history. The Separatists, working with nefarious corporate organizations, are stunned not only by the decisiveness of the hitherto stagnant Republic, but moreover by its use of a trained and well-equipped clone army. At the battle's turning point, the troopships land to disgorge swarms of armed transport gunships under the cover of turbolaser fire. The ships are accompanied by heavy ground vehicles and thousands of well-trained, dedicated clone troops.

BORN FROM BETRAYAL

The new Galactic Army's arsenal was secretly built by a mighty corporation that could have led the Separatists if not for bloody treachery. Leading Kuati executives were assassinated when Neimoidians took over the Trade Federation at the notorious Eriadu Conference a decade earlier. The outraged industrialists have since aligned with the Supreme Chancellery. Meanwhile, the pace of clandestine construction accelerates in Kuat's cordoned shipyards and factories on Rothana.

Bridge and battle operations rooms are furnished with sophisticated holographic displays

Conning tower scanner and communications housing

Power core is not subject to artificial gravity

Assembly hall

Power systems maintenance vent

Dorsal turbolaser emplacement

Engine servicing release latches

Power systems cooling neutrino radiator grille

Antigrav repulsorlift generator

Tensorial integrity field conduits

Tail houses extended spinal conduit for inertial compensator fields

Hyperdrive generator

Electromagnetic thrust-vectoring panels

Auxiliary thruster greatly affects turning due to further off-axis location

Thruster particle stream channel

Smaller lower hangar receives clone troops

Action-ready gunships drop through hatch facing forward

Antigrav repulsorlifts support most of the ship's weight, but landing pads provide stable ground contact

SHAPE OF THINGS TO COME

In the peaceful centuries preceding the Clone Wars, many larger and more powerful warships were built to defend rich industrialized sectors of Corellia, Humbarine, and Kuat, but their hyperdrive jump ranges were local. The return of truly trans-galactic warships and armies is an ominous innovation.

Main reactor is hidden within hull terraces, unlike the bulbous ventral protrusions of more powerful ships

Brim notch improves clearance of cannons and shield circulation

Condensed annihilation reactant is denser than ship's bulk by many orders of magnitude

Starboard dorsal conduits of inertial compensator and tensorial integrity fields

Reactant channels lead to reactor system

Gunships circulating on rail undergo basic maintenance

Heavy strategic missile and torpedo launch tubes

Most habitable decks are near dorsal terrace

LAAT/c cargo carrier gunship

Reactant valve module

Superstructure frame

Logics reception bay

AT-TE Walker

Subsidiary reactor

Turbolift shaft

Logistics hangar hatch

Logics reception bay

Front landing pad

Bulk transit shaft

Point-defense laser cannon

AT-TEs stand ready at front of bays, with SPHA-T vehicles stored behind

Enemy fusion rockets barely score the super-dispersive neutronium-impregnated hull cladding

NEW WAVE

The vessels that ensured victory at Geonosis are sure to be copied by other shipbuilders loyal to the Republic. Already the Arch-Provost of Rendili and the Commissars of Grizmallt have ordered countless industrial spies and starship designers to reduce Kuat's competitive lead for the Galactic Republic's new contracts. Rendili's extensive system of smaller shipyards across the Mid and Outer Rims of the galaxy are a strong advantage that may give them temporary ascendancy.

Barracks

Heavy combat vehicle service bay

Gunship boarding platform

Regional shield generator node

Fuel inlet manifold

White hazard marks surround apertures

Service lift platform descends to lower bay

Ramp extended

Each battalion marches in rows with two squads

SUPPORTIVE MOTHERSHIP

Each *Acclamator* coordinates its forces strategically. Orbital bombardments with high-yield proton torpedoes and surgical turbolaser strikes hit enemy fortifications when capture is not a priority. Armies entrenched deep underground may be subject to a last-resort "Base Delta Zero" fleet bombardment. Such operations reduce the upper crust of a planet to molten slag.

Troops Assemble On Coruscant, thousands of clone troopers board Republic assault ships that will deliver them into battle.

Venerable
emblem of
Galactic Republic
unity

Powered, superdispersive
inner-armor spreads
impact of enemy fire across
entire hull

Repulsorlift array
power conduits

Laser cannon power
feeds

Yellow mark of
aircrew helmet

Maintenance diagnostics
computer access hatches

Cockpit capsule
umbilical cables

Escape capsule's
lower separation
surface

Clamp releases when
escape capsule ejects

Red warning light
indicates rear hold
doors are open

Crew ladders fold into
ceiling

Laser cannons clear
ground resistance with
variable shots of up to five
gigajoules

IM-6 Medical Droid

Medical and survival
gear stored in lockers

Laser cannon discharge
stimulators

Flexible power cable
connects to swivelling laser
cannon

Forward laser cannon
power convertor and
capacitor array

Entry to troop
hold

Fuselage main
repulsor-vane array

Wing turrets roll in any direction,
but socket contact provides
stability

Assault Transport The heavy weapons of the LAAT/i are vital for clearing a path through
enemy forces in which to deploy troops and vehicles—their fundamental function.

INTEGRATED BATTLEDRESS

A clone trooper's full combat armor is the basis of
an integrated system in which the gunships are
vital links. Individual troopers can receive
command signals and relay status signals via this
system. Troops also share tactical video from their
helmet visors, with multispectral imaging that
penetrates smoke, fog, and the airborne soil of the
most explosive battlezones. The airtight and
thermally regulated body glove is impervious to
germ and chemical agents, and provides protection
in space and hostile atmospheres. The armor's
heat resistance allows troopers to stride through
the searing interfaces of theater shields like
lifeless battle droids, as well as deflecting
glancing blaster shots and damping direct hits
enough to improve the wearer's chances of survival.

SCOUT SPEEDER BIKES

A rack of one-person military speeder bikes fits
into the tail of troop-carrier gunships. To deploy
them, the gunship descends to a sheltered and
tactically useful site. Once below their altitude
limit, these fast but relatively delicate scout
vehicles emerge through the rear hatch. Riders fly
ahead for reconnaissance or to secure the flanks
and wake of the battle lines.

Missile feed ventilation

Flat wing is not aerodynamic, but aids balance and mounts attitude-control repulsors

Engine air intake

Missile belt

Missile chute frictionless sheath

Each blast-effect missile concentrates its 100-kiloton explosion in a two-degree cone

Force-field effects of powerful inertial compensator keep the hold interior jolt-free, enabling troops to ride in standing posture

Power feed to launchers

Power generator

Outer armor

Aft power feeds

[A]tmospheric [con]ditioner

Handle to slide open door when unpowered

Speeder-bike [p]annier

Recon speeder-bike [r]ack

Tail ramp lowered for speeder-bike deployment

One platoon of heavy infantry clone troops ready to dismount

Maintenance hatch

Heavy blaster rifle uses video gunsight display in helmet visor and has effective range of 10 kilometers (6 miles) when mounted in tripod

Emergency fire-retardant piping

Coolant gas vent

Turret gunner is fully armored because of exposed position

AT-TE

The intimidating All Terrain Tactical Enforcer is an assault vehicle that offers support to the Republic's clone army, obliterating threats to friendly infantry and reinforcing tactical control. Wading through the savage din of battle, the walker's sure-footed, six-legged stance allows it to cross crevices and climb otherwise impassably rugged slopes. Its massive turret-mounted missile-launcher bombards fixed emplacements or smites slow-moving aircraft, while six laser-cannon turrets swivel quickly to devastate faster line-of-sight targets.

LAND CONTROL

Unlike fast-flying aircraft and fighters, each AT-TE exerts a persistently formidable presence on the ground. AT-TEs take possession of territory and equalize the struggle between clone soldiers and the Separatists' war machines. For rapid deployment of troops, AT-TE walkers can ride an LAAT/c cargo gunship to the battlefront. With their passenger cargo unloaded, walkers then hunt down enemies at a more rapid pace.

Vents reduce nozzle pressure effects on emerging projectile

Mass-driver barrel accelerates projectile

Mass-driver coils and waste heat radiator

Top hatch

Exterior gunner with full armor protection

Target screen

Ladder

Elevation axle

Ammunition belt

Canopy opens up at hinge

Periscope and rangefinder

Spotter finds targets and coordinates gunners

Driver

Full armor worn by vehicle crews restricts movement (not enough time before the Battle of Geonosis for crew uniform modifications)

Bar pivots down to give crew a step up into cabin

Laser cannon stimulator forward elements

Laser cannon power feeds

Targeting computer

Notches for holding clamps in hangar

Laser cannon charger/ transformer

Inertial compensator generator under seats

Close Combat In the event of an assault by enemy infantry, an AT-TE can dismount its two squads of troops to enter the fray and secure the immediate surroundings.

Flexible "concertina" section houses power generators

Seat restraints steady troops in event of inertial compensator failure

Power lines

Passage to rear hull

Laser cannon turrets defend walker's rear

Life-support air reprocessor

Conductive armor spreads heat of enemy fire to minimize penetration

Tail gun maintenance access panel

Targeting controls

Left tail gunner

Rear-leg actuator shaft

Stance mimics the sturdy form of the arctic horny whelmer of Rothana

Left-rear hatch

Toe actuator

Leg engine housing

Highly movable floating shoulder supports

Servomotor discs rotate with leg movement

Ankle-locking clamp

Foreleg actuator piston

Foot orientation pistons

Steps

Hatch opens downward to act as a boarding ramp

Ammo hatch

Exceptionally powerful clone trooper blaster rifles

Widely spread footing gives AT-TE excellent stability

Ammunition storage for main cannon; troops reload ammo belts manually

Terrain sensors

EFFECTIVE DESIGN

In years to come, the success of the AT-TE will lead to heavier designs, such as the towering AT-AT (All Terrain Armored Transport) and AT-HE (All Terrain Heavy Enforcer). These craft will incorporate hulls that are raised above the reach of exploding mines, and give greater vantage for their energy weapons.

PRODUCT OF ROTHANA

When devising armaments and vehicles for clone troops, the Kaminoans subcontracted the secret job to Rothana Heavy Engineering, a subsidiary of Kuat Drive Yards—and no friend of the Trade Federation or Techno Union. Toiling in immense underground factories and honeycombed orbital shipyards, RHE's workforce is famed for its diligence. Their star system is uniquely clear of Trade Federation espionage, due to factors ranging from the impenetrably complex Rothanian etiquette (which makes outsiders stand out) to a sizeable KDY corporate-security starfleet and inventively deployed mines in Rothana's inbound hyperlanes.

INCISIVE VANGUARD

AT-TEs are effective at penetrating powerful energy shields. Walker movement uses simple surface traction, whereas the high-velocity exhausts that drive a speeder or starship are stifled by particle shields. Furthermore, flying craft can be damaged by energy discharges leaping from the ground at shield interfaces, but a walker's natural grounding provides invulnerability against this effect. AT-TEs are also well-shielded against electromagnetic pulse weapons and ion cannon fire.

LAAT/C GUNSHIP

Rothana Heavy Engineering's Low-Altitude Assault Transport/
carrier (LAAT/c) is a variant of the LAAT/i gunship, and was
initially designed to carry heavy AT-TEs to the front lines. The
design was modified to make it more versatile, allowing it to
transport a variety of payloads, including forward command
centers, portable power generators, and shield generators. The
LAAT/c is crewed by a single pilot, and has a rapid cargo-deployment
system that features magnetic clamps to hold heavy payloads in
place. The clamps can be instantly disengaged, allowing the
carrier to lift off without time-consuming offloading operations.

AUTOMATIC ASCENT

The moment an LAAT/c gunship's arms release their hold on an
AT-TE, the sudden weight loss causes the LAAT/c to rise rapidly
from the drop-off point. Because such sudden ascents would be
jarring to most life forms in ordinary repulsorlift ships, the LAAT/c
has strong anti-gravity compensators in the cockpit and passenger
areas to ensure pilots and crew remain unaffected.

Heavy Hauler LAAT/c cargo gunships have reinforced frames and more powerful repulsorlift
engines than standard gunships, enabling them to carry cumbersome AT-TE walkers.
Cargo gunships are also used to transport mobile tactical command stations into battle.

Air Support An AT-TE hits the ground
walking after an LAAT/c cargo gunship
delivers it to a planetary surface. The
gunship provides further support by
firing at enemy targets that pose the
most immediate threat to the AT-TE.

SOLAR SAILERS

ount Dooku, as a man of learning, was long aware of the
Geonosians' ancient sailing traditions when they offered to build
a new personal craft for him. In early times, these insectoid engineers
built cargo kites that flew in the dense air of their low-gravity world.
Their first spacecraft were huge, gossamer-thin robotic sheets that
sailed on the power of sunshine, followed by more hefty craft pushed
from home by intense laser beams. The use of solar sailers declined as
the Geonosians discovered modern fusion technologies—although
Poggle the Lesser, Archduke of Geonosis, was pleased to draw on
ancient technology in order to accommodate an esteemed ally.

*Sail is 112.5 m (369 ft) wide and
composed of exotic matter that reflects
otherwise undetectable energies*

*Sail is 67.1 m
(220 ft) high*

*Mast is
105.2 m
(345 ft) long*

*Receptor
nodule*

Geonosis Launch Chute A tubular
launch chute built within the wall
of an abandoned weapons factory
provides an escape route for Count
Dooku's Solar Sailer. A combination
of exotic tractor-beam technology
and small repulsors embedded
within the chute's walls enable
ships to be ejected at high speed.

SAIL POWER

The delicate reflector-surfaces of most "solar" sails unfurl to
moon-like diameters, and are more commonly pushed by
tachyon streams and ultraviolet lasers than sunlight. Dooku's
unique solar sailer, however, achieves similar performance
across the entire galaxy with a much smaller span and no
detectable support system.

Stealth System
Dooku's Solar Sailer
carries a prototype
Sienar Design Systems
sensor array, which
can deceive the most
sophisticated
detection systems.

Solar Sail The unexplained
mobility of Dooku's Solar Sailer
enhances his commanding
mystique in Geonosian eyes.

Pilot Droid Instead of relying on an automatic pilot system to operate his Solar Sailer, Count Dooku uses an FA-4 pilot droid that was manufactured by the SoroSuub Corporation.

BOW PRONGS

Geonosian starships typically feature two or more multi-functional bow prongs. Rows of narrow-beam tractor/repulsor emitters along the prongs act as offensive grapples or steering aids when there are surrounding objects to pull and push against. Also, the spread of ray-shield energies around the prongs can be selectively adjusted to give the ship extra maneuverablity.

Yard joint

Collapsed main mast

Power lines to portside dorsal beam elements

Dorsal sail carapace

Dark surface made of heavy metals that are preciously rare on Geonosis

Motorized unfolding sail nexus

Intermediary power cell

FA-4 Pilot Droid

Levers deploy sail

Cockpit module can be replaced by a weapons or sensor orb if piloting controls are routed to main hold

Main console

Prong elements diagnostics hatch

Permeable covers over beamer elements

Shield projectors

MYSTERIOUS ANTIQUE

After leaving the Jedi Order, Dooku developed a taste for rare pre-Republic artifacts. An antiques dealer near the Gree Enclave sold him an ancient sail, with unique and startling properties. The sail is powered by an as-yet undetectable source of supralight emissions, allowing Dooku's custom ship an independence unknown by any other current space-faring vehicle.

Power feed

Dooku's chair rises from longitudinal access shaft

Tractor/repulsor emitter element

Furled ventral sail

Frame

Inertial compensator

Conventional scanner array

Repulsorlift generator

Landing-gear actuators

Last segment is jointed to spread ship's weight

Secret Hangar After landing his Solar Sailer in a hangar in the abandoned LiMerge Power building on Coruscant, Dooku has a clandestine meeting with Darth Sidious.

DOOKU'S SOLAR SAILER

A gift from his Geonosian colleagues, Dooku's ship is a unique melding of a *Punworcca 116*-class sloop with an elegant sail supplied by the Count himself. On Dooku's instructions, Geonosian engineers attached this enigmatic accessory to the ship to provide independent power without the need to carry fuel (apart from guide thrusters). The ship's interior is tailored to Dooku's sense of refinement, with an extensive databook library and ornate decorations.

Computer consoles and strategic chart displays

Count Dooku in main hold

Databook library

Hyperdrive segments are charged by power receptors for jumps to and from hyperspace

Power receptors channel recharging energies to power cells

Sail can configure to focus onto any of the four special-purpose nodules

Reactant tanklets

Engineering console

Ship's status scent-stimulator vent

Thruster propellant feed

Guide thruster

Reactor shield

Portside reactor core

Ladder to maintenance station

Airlock console

Passenger orb is non-rotating but replaceable with some effort

Inner airlock doors

Door light

Outer airlock hatch

Retracting boarding ramp

Life-support

Horizontal hull seam for overhaul servicing

Laminar inter-hull

Passenger bunk privacy drapes

Transceiver nodule

Viewport

Personal locker

EPISODE III
REVENGE OF THE SITH

The Clone Wars have escalated into a cataclysmic conflict, with the Republic's Jedi Knights and clone troops engaged in desperate campaigns across the galaxy. The Separatist movement, now known as the Confederacy of Independent Systems, is encircling the crumbling Galactic Republic, advancing ever-nearer to the star systems of the Galactic Core. Neither side is aware that their leaders are secretly in league. The Republic's Supreme Chancellor Palpatine is really the Sith Lord Darth Sidious, and his apprentice is Darth Tyranus, otherwise known as Count Dooku, the leader of the Separatists. Sidious is merely playing for time until he is ready to replace Tyranus with a new, more powerful apprentice, who will help him to achieve his ultimate aim: absolute control of the galaxy under Sith rule and the formation of a merciless new order—the Galactic Empire.

STAR DESTROYER- VENATOR CLASS

The Galactic Republic's new *Venator*-class Star Destroyer is fast enough to chase down blockade runners and big enough to lead independent missions such as the liberation of Utapau. A flotilla of these medium-weight, versatile multi-role warships can blast through the shields of a Trade Federation battleship with ease. The hangars of the *Venator*-class are much larger than older Star Destroyers like the *Victory*-class, and can support hundreds of fightercraft. The ship is also capable of planetary landings as a military transport and can act as an escort in the Republic armada. However, the primary function of the *Venator*-class is its role as a fighting ship and starfighter carrier, making it a firm favorite with Jedi pilots.

Orbital Defender
Venator-class Star Destroyers become a common sight in the skies and orbit of Coruscant during the Clone Wars, and protect the capital planet from numerous Separatist attacks.

Annihilation reactant silo

Markings of Fifth Fleet in Open Circle armada

Heavy turbolaser turret

Hangar door track

Hangar command post

Standard complement includes 192 V-wings

Atmosphere containment shield projectors line door

Open Circle armada's emblem

Flight deck runs parallel to dorsal ridge

Venator *typically holds 36 ARC-170 fighters*

Eta-2 Actis Interceptor

LAAT/c (Low-Altitude Assault Transport/carrier)

LAAT/i (Low-Altitude Assault Transport/infantry) gunship can deploy when ship is in atmospheric flight

ARC (Aggressive ReCon)-170 fighter on hangar approach

Fighter and vehicle hangars

Local shield generator

Medium dual turbolaser

Ventral docking bay (on the initiative of General Skywalker, some Venator-class ships feature additional SPHA-T laser cannons here to increase ventral firepower)

Hull scarring caused by direct impact from a crashing Separatist tri-fighter

Atmosphere ducts

Dorsal doors— powerful deflector shields also protect the ship's interior

Bow tractor beam projector

Tractor beam generator

Crewed areas

AT-TE (All Terrain Tactical Enforcer) walker

Starfighter flight control bridge

Helm and command bridges

Main reactor annihilates up to 40,000 tons of fuel per second at maximum power

Reactant pumps and ducts

Tower decks run parallel to dorsal ridge

Hyperwave comm/scanner

Hyperdrive generator

Main inertial compressor

Stern power feeds

Ion drive thrusters

Electromagnetic plates at nozzle bend thrust streams to steer ship

Subsidiary reactor

Power cells

Portside docking vestibule

Light laser cannons defend against fast enemy fighters

Brim and hull decks run horizontally

Regional deflector shield generator

Docking port mates with a space station, mooring tower or larger starship for transfer of equipment and troops

Port flank power spine

Crane for securing a docked ship or moving freight

Crewed areas

THE KUAT LEGACY

Kuat Drive Yards, the manufacturer of the *Venator*-class, claim the Republic is winning the Clone Wars with this ship and their other powerful, wedge-shaped vessels. But the construction of *Venator*-class vessels is already slowing in favor of more robust, mile-long *Imperator*-class (renamed *Imperial*-class after the Jedi Purge) and hangarless *Tector*-class Star Destroyers. These ships will see service for decades to come, as the Republic is transformed into the Empire. The Imperial Starfleet will justify its existence in unending war against Separatist holdouts, dissident rebels and even, it is rumored, deterring barbarian invaders from outside the galaxy.

CARRIER ROLE

The long dorsal flight deck of the *Venator*-class enables hundreds of starfighters to launch rapidly. The slow opening and closing of the deck's armored bow doors, however, can leave the vessel vulnerable. This weakness is compensated for by strong deflector shielding around the deck's entrance, but the design flaw will be eliminated in future Star Destroyers.

Star Destroyer Hangar Inside a hangar on the *Venator*-class Star Destroyer *Vigilance*, Jedi General Obi-Wan Kenobi briefs members of the 212th Attack Battalion, prior to their mission to the Utapau system.

REPUBLIC FIREPOWER

Despite numerous victories over the Confederacy during the Clone Wars, the Republic becomes increasingly aware of the fact that their enemies can produce scores of battle droids much faster than Kaminoan cloners can produce soldiers, who also require training. To compensate for this disparity, Republic-allied engineers ensure Star Destroyers can be operated by a relatively small crew, and weapons designers have created more powerful turbolaser cannons with increased range and accuracy, giving the Republic Navy a strong advantage against Confederate warships.

Star Destroyer Gun Deck Specially trained clone troopers man the laser cannons on *Venator*-Class Star Destroyers.

Dangerous Duty Being part of a Star Destroyer gun crew is notoriously hazardous, as they suffer high casualty rates.

HEAVY-DUTY TURBOLASERS

A *Venator*-class Star Destroyer's eight DBY-827 heavy turbolaser turrets are the standard requirement in naval gunnery for intense inter-ship combat and planetary bombardment. The DBY-827's precise, long-range tracking mode enables it to hit a target vessel at distances of over ten light-minutes, while the turret can rotate in three seconds in its close-fighting, fast-tracking mode. Seven different blast intensities provide a choice between crippling shots and outright vaporization of the enemy. The *Venator*-class, as a true warship, can feed almost its entire reactor output to its heavy guns when required.

Capacitors store energy and discharge it to the gun

Cooling fins

Crew lift

Fire control room

Tracking sensors

Flexible power feeds

Vents for spent coolants and gases

Elevation pivot

Energy-dissipating hull armor

Turbolaser barrel

Atmosphere duct

Main longitudinal power line

Local tensor field guides help bolster ship structure

Crew corridor

Turret rotation base

Power feeds to turret rotation mechanisms

Broadside Combat The Separatist flagship *Invisible Hand* is pounded into a flaming hulk at point-blank range by the Star Destroyer *Guarlara*.

V-WING

One of the newer and more numerous fightercraft defending the Galactic Republic, V-wings are sharp, compact support ships deployed in epic fleet actions or in defense of fortress worlds. Launched in furious swarms from the Republic's carriers and warships, these fast, agile starfighters are frustratingly elusive targets and their swiveling twin laser cannons make them surprising and deadly opponents. V-wings are piloted by a single clone trooper backed up by an independent Q7-series astromech droid. Like many models mass-produced for Loyalist forces, V-wings are too compact for a hyperdrive, but carry a powerful reactor and use two vertically placed ion drive thrusters for astonishingly fast pitch-turns.

Strength in Numbers Streamlined mass production techniques prompted the V-wing to replace the V-19 Torrent as the preferred compact space superiority fighter.

DOGFIGHTER SPECIAL

Developed by Kuat Systems Engineering, the same company that produced Jedi starfighters, the Alpha-3 Nimbus V-wing utilizes cutting-edge technology for maneuverability, making it far more nimble than an ARC-170, and the best choice for clone pilots to engage in dogfights against speedy vulture droids and tri-fighters. Bracketing the wedge-shaped V-wing are a set of flat wings extending above and below the ship. The wings are on articulated collars that allow them to rotate 90 degrees for landing. Two pairs of laser cannons are mounted on the wing struts, providing the V-wing with rapid-fire capability.

Deflector shield heat sinks

Thruster

Radiator panels aid heat disposal during intense activity

Spherical Q7-series astro-droid copilot aids navigation and in-flight maintenance

Sealed flightsuit equips pilot for possible ejection

Comm/scan processors

Forward sensors

Laser cannons swivel on wing hubs

Repulsorlift vanes

Laser cannon capacitors and power feed

Reactant tank

Shield projector units

Power lines to shield projectors

Wing radiators unfolded in flight position

Forward Cannons The ARC-170's forward laser cannons can easily punch through reinforced durasteel plating on enemy ships. The cannons are usually fired by the copilot but control can also be turned over to the pilot.

Tail gunner

Dorsal tail cannon

Gunnery controls

R2-series astro-droid

Steps

Copilot/forward gunner

Coolant ducts

Hyperdrive

Pilot is a veteran Fett clone, but newer lineages are bred from proven ace pilot recruits

Power feed to hyperdrive

Ventral tail cannon

Thruster nozzle

Ion acceleration chamber

Fuel tanks

The ARC-170's deflector shields disperse the heat generated by air resistance in atmospheric flight, enabling the craft to reach hypersonic speeds

Cooling vents

Power trunk leading back to generators

Closed louvres over retro-thrusters

Heraldic emblem awarded to Kenobi's and Skywalker's fleet

Front deflector shield projectors

Power feed to deflectors

Forward repulsorlift

Cannon diagnostic wiring

Cooling ducts for laser cannon

EQUIPPED FOR DANGER

The ARC-170's characteristic split transverse wings unfold and splay to expose the heat sinks and active radiators which aid the fighter's shielding and thermal stability during battle or hot pursuit. The heavy nose section houses a diverse and sensitive array of long-range sensors, scanners, and jammers, ideal for dangerous scout missions. The ship resembles other Incom and Subpro fighting craft commonly used by Republic forces in the Outer Rim. Notable cousins include the heavier PTB-625 and NTB-630 planetary and naval bombers, as well as the lighter, popular one-man Z-95 *Headhunter* fighter (which will lead to a successor, the T-65 X-wing).

Power cables to laser cannon

Heat sink and cooling radiator panels

Torque field currents spin-align and concentrate the blaster beam's energy

Muzzle can internally tilt the beam a few degrees off-axis for precise aim

Layers of superconductor and nano-ducts for tibanna coolant

Powerful oscillations of unified energy fields build beam intensity inside the resonance chamber

Sturdy structural casing

Waste heat sink

Radiator surface

Winglets open for efficient heat disposal to cool weapons and engines during combat

Targeting rangefinder

Recharge port

Maintenance cover

Flight computer

Communications and sensor processor

Jamming device

Gamma-ray imaging spectro-photometer

Long-wave antenna

Active scanner modules

Starboard passive sensor

Headlight

Dedicated energy receptor

Forward landing gear

BEST OF THE BRAVE

The Open Circle fleet, led by Generals Kenobi and Skywalker, carries thousands of ARC-170s and other fighters that have endured harrowing months of continual war in the cruel Outer Rim sieges. Amongst the most experienced of ARC-170 squadrons is Squad Seven, a disciplined team of veteran aviators known for their unwavering courage. Squad Seven are clones of Jango Fett, the bounty hunter who was the genetic model for the first clone troops. However, an increasing number of units are formed from rigorously selected volunteers. Over the coming years, the most accomplished volunteer aces will be honored as stock for new clone lineages, and distinguished with all-black dress uniforms.

ARC-170 Cockpit Although the widely spaced data displays in the ARC-170 cockpit would baffle most humans, they were designed for clone pilots with superior peripheral vision.

ARC-170 FIGHTER

Rugged and durable, the ARC-170 (Aggressive ReConnaissance) fighter is designed to undertake the loneliest, independent, manned patrols or daring raids, as it penetrates deep into hostile sectors. With its inbuilt hyperdrive and capacity for a droid navigator, this long-range craft is built for days of unsupported interstellar missions, which vitally extends the reach of the Jedi and their starfleet beyond warships and carrier-dependent fighters. The ARC-170's main laser cannons are uncommonly large and blazingly effective against larger opponents. Robust armor, shields, and tail guns improve the odds of survival when the ship is surrounded by dozens or even hundreds of light, evasive droid fighters. When piloted into battle alongside agile V-wings and Jedi Interceptors, heavy-punching ARC-170 squadrons complete a formidable strike-force mix.

Squad Seven The foremost ARC-170 squadron in the Open Circle Fleet, Squad Seven is led by clone Commander Davijaan, who flies under the call sign "Odd Ball."

JEDI DARING

By shunning protective flight-suits, Anakin and Obi-Wan set a brave example to inspire their clone pilots. A small breach in the canopy or ejection into space would spell certain death. Leading from the front has killed many Jedi in the last two years. However, the remaining Jedi assert that exhibiting fighting spirit and leadership gives an unbeatable combat advantage. The stubborn survival of the Loyalists in the fight against ever greater droid forces may prove that "size matters not" indeed.

Flight controls

Expansive viewports provide maximum all-round visibiity

Spacious cockpit

R2-D2 acts as copilot or helps lock onto targets

Monitors

Joystick

Exposed inner surfaces or radiator

Headrest

Canopy hinge

Heat exchanger

Stowage space

Life-support components

High-power reactor

Kill markings, equivalent to tri-fighter squadron

Flight control connections

Inertial compensators

Stern landing pad

Electrostatic plates around thruster nozzles

Electromagnetic vectoring deflects thrust stream by up to 30 degrees for versatile steering

Ion impulsion chamber accelerates invisible, diffuse particle stream up to near-light speeds

Double arc emblem celebrates Republic fleet under Kenobi and Skywalker's leadership

Minimal repulsorlift projectors used for taking off and landing

Starboard power cell

Coolant feeds between radiators and heat exchanger

Exposed area is potential target for buzz droid sabotage

JEDI INTERCEPTOR

Reduced form of Jedi Bendu-inspired emblem used in Unification Wars that formed the Galactic Republic over 25,000 years ago

Laser cannons fire glowing, strobing beams of massless energy

Long barrel provides amplified yield and exceptional range

Starboard bow landing pad

Lid over pop-up headlight

Hydraulic rams actuate landing gear

Emergency toolkit

Ion cannon fires plasma bursts causing electric disruption to target

Energy capacitors

Hidden outer radiator surface

Radiator wings open during intense dogfight action

Anakin's Eta-2 was painted yellow at his request, allegedly in tribute to his boyhood podracer

Superficial wing armor

Racing home from the brutal Outer Rim sieges to rescue the kidnapped Supreme Chancellor Palpatine, Obi-Wan Kenobi and Anakin Skywalker waste no time scrambling to their fighters. Leading the Republic's aerial forces in their Jedi Interceptors, they flit through the battle-zone with astonishing agility. Their spacecraft's compact design is suited to the Force-assisted tactical abilities of Jedi pilots—heavy flight instruments, sensors, and shields are unnecessary. Over the last three years, the distinctive Interceptor profile has become a symbol of authority and hope for the Republic's clone forces, and a frustrating apparition to the Separatists.

AGILE ADVERSARY

In the last battles of the Clone Wars, some Jedi Knights fly one of the lightest, most agile fighters designed in millennia. Hardly larger than the average airspeeder, the Eta-2 *Actis* Interceptor enjoys superior speed and maneuverability compared to the already tiny Delta-7 *Aethersprite*. Compacting a fighter's intense power into a tiny hull made overheating a challenge—which was met by an extensive system of heat sinks, pumps, and radiator wings. The Interceptor's large laser cannons fire intense beams, but its modest capacitors limit continuous fire. This is not usually a handicap for Jedi pilots, who rarely waste a shot.

Customized Controls Each Jedi Interceptor's cockpit controls and data displays are custom fitted for the individual pilot.

Jedi Wingmates
Because Obi-Wan Kenobi strongly dislikes piloting, and Anakin has always been a natural behind the controls of vehicles, their relationship as master and apprentice becomes somewhat reversed in space combat.

HYPERDRIVE BOOSTERS

Because many Republic starfighters are too small to safely contain a hyperdrive, the fighters must connect to external hyperdrive boosters. Kuat Systems Engineering designed the Delta-7 *Aethersprite* light interceptor, Alpha-3 Nimbus V-wing starfighter, and Eta-2 *Actis* Interceptor with docking clamps for hyperdrive booster rings, and data-feeds that enable the starfighters' astromechs to transmit hyperspace coordinates to the rings' computers. The rings are manufactured by TransGalMeg Industries, Inc. of the Rayter sector, a subcontractor of Kuat.

ORBITAL DEPOTS

The Republic Navy has pools of hyperdrive booster rings stationed in orbit around Coruscant and other worlds, for the use of Jedi starfighters in their fleet. The rings are serviced by technical support droids, which are engineered to operate in zero gravity.

SYLIURE-31 BOOSTER

Powered by twin reactors and ion drives, the Syliure-31 hyperspace docking ring is a class of hyperdrive booster that contains "hypermatter," providing ballast for the attached starfighter during the jump to hyperspace. When traveling at hyperspeed, shields protect the ship and booster against potentially fatal collisions with interstellar gas and dark particles. Stasis fields also act to slow the passage of onboard time, ensuring that the pilot ages only as fast as the rest of the galaxy.

Ion drive thruster nozzle

Kenobi in Interceptor

Dense hypermatter spins through ring

Forward shield projector module

Link to flight controls

Ion acceleration pod

Heat surge radiator

Starboard reactor

Hyperdrive motivator

Variant models are fitted with extra acceleration pods

Port stasis field generator

Socket fits bow of several Jedi starfighter models

Docking Procedure As the starfighter glides toward the booster ring, the ring's compact tractor beam projectors help guide the fighter directly into the docking socket.

Two orbital tech-support droids monitor the docking procedure, and ensure that the starfighter secures to the ring properly.

Conceived as an improvement on the Syliure-31 hyperspace docking ring, the Syliure-45 has four additional ion acceleration pods.

CONFEDERACY BUZZ DROID

During the Battle of Coruscant, Confederacy tri-fighters defend General Grievous's stricken flagship by harassing Jedi attackers with special new ordnance. Launched from modified tri-fighters and other vessels, these guided buzz droid missiles are lethal, and able to outturn and outrun nearly any manned starship. But their aim is not a direct kill. Instead of detonating on impact, the missile delivers a swarm of buzz droids: mechanical gremlins expertly programmed in the fine arts of technological sabotage.

Homing and guidance instruments

Heat exchanger

Droid dispenser ram

Reactor

Instrumentation heat sink/ radiator

Dormant buzz droids

Fuel pods (empty within two minutes of launch)

Waste gas outlet

Stabiliser fins maintain course in atmospheric flight

Thruster can accelerate beyond 10,000G and tilt for tight turns

BUZZ DROID MISSILE

Aggressive droid brain loaded with target-ship schematics and a destructive attitude

Communications antenna for remote control and coordinating attacks with other buzz droids

Hull cutaway for thrusters

Protective layers absorb heat and impacts

Heat-dissipating layer helps passage through target-ship's shields

Hull cut-aways allow droid's photoreceptor "eyes" to see during flight

Shock-absorbing outer shell

Subsurface radiator

SMALL BUT DEADLY

Tiny maneuvering thrusters and a protective, shielded shell enable the buzz droid to slip through a target ship's shields and onto its hull. Once "hatched," each buzz droid deploys an array of graspers and cutting tools to cause the maximum damage. Each buzz droid's brain is loaded with the design schematics of a vast range of starships and military targets, enabling it to identify weak points. These highly effective attackers succeed in crippling General Kenobi's Jedi Interceptor. Dealing with buzz droids is highly difficult, as firing on them is likely to damage or destroy their intended victim. Removing them may require an allied pilot to fly in close and literally sweep off the droids.

Sensory processors

Four tiny sublight thrusters help droid steer onto its prey

Miniature reactor primed for self-destruct

Plasma cutting torch

Main eye with multiple lenses and filters

Secondary eyes aid spatial awareness

X-ray sensor

Pincer

Drill head

Extendable probe can invade computers and control systems

Puncture and cutting tool

Actuator

BUZZ DROID

Hook appendage

Circular saw

Magnetic footpad helps droid cling to hull

Buzz Attack A team of buzz droids typically targets a starfighter's astromech first, and can easily carve up a starfighter's hull in less than a minute.

TRI-FIGHTER

Cunning and eerily determined, droid tri-fighters are frightening new defenders of the Separatist battle fleets. These fast, agile space-superiority fighters are built to excel in dogfighting. Equipped with more advanced droid brains than common Trade Federation Vulture droid fighters, tri-fighters pose a challenge to even the best organic starpilots. They may be outrun by high-speed Jedi Interceptors, but they are bulkier and more heavily armed, which makes them a force to be reckoned with.

Tri-Fighters Over Coruscant Chasing down Republic starfighters during an orbital battle, a tri-fighter aims its cannons and opens fire.

COLICOID DESIGN

The tri-fighter's fearsome appearance and predatory programming is the work of the Colicoids—the creators of the Trade Federation's droideka heavy infantry. The ridged, three-armed design is based on the skull features of a terrifying prehistoric predator native to the planet Colla IV. Three independent thrusters give the craft its agility, and a powerful reactor and control/comms transceiver provide unusual range for a droid fighter.

Six re-arranged triangles from the Confederacy emblem signify the tri-fighter's squadron

Aggressive droid brain surrounding nose cannon's capacitor

COORDINATED ATTACK

Unlike Trade Federation Vulture droid starfighters, which are controlled entirely by signals from a Droid Control Ship computer, tri-fighters have droid brains engineered with basic heuristic processors, which enable them to analyze, anticipate, and mimic enemy tactics. Tri-fighters can enter combat independently or link their intelligence systems to coordinate multi-fighter attacks on a single target.

Droid Onslaught A trio of tri-fighters poses a definite threat to a single starfighter, although Jedi pilots can usually evade or destroy them.

Wing laser cannons can fire together or independently (cannon can tilt or slide on rail slightly to improve its deadly converging aim)

Support clamps lock cannon in place if fighter is firing while flying a twisting course

Cables from power cells to weapon capacitor

Continually charging capacitor feeds the laser cannon's rapid bursts of fire

Radiator surface

Sturdy internal frame

Fuel tank

Propellant delivery

Power and propellant regulation computer

Repulsorlift aids flying over planetary surfaces

Chain of power cells line inside of wing

Ionization reactor

Reactor's magnetic confinement elements

Rotating frame holds reactor

Main reactor core

Initial ion acceleration chamber

Nose laser cannon is fixed in place

Electrodes

Barrel cooling blades

Secondary accelerator adds spin to ion stream

Left-eye photoreceptor

Discharge unit

Particle stream exits thrust nozzle at near-light speed

Heat sinks grille inside radiator fin

Sensitive communications dish maintains a strong fix on mothership signal

Target scanner

Missile support rods fold out from wing

Clamps holding portside buzz-droid missile

X- and gamma-ray projector cluster

Cooling radiator

Missile carrying special payload of lethal saboteur buzz droids

Thin panelled segment exposes fuel to emit excess radiation

STABLE SHOOTING

Designed and built by Baktoid Fleet Ordnance, the HMP (Heavy Missile Platform) droid gunship has a heavy, weapon-laden front end. Powerful repulsorlift arrays provide stability, ensuring the HMP's lethal effectiveness both in skirmishes and as a hovering gun platform over ground battles. High-powered shields in its saucer-like hull deflect and absorb all but the most powerful laser blasts. Forward thrust is provided by ion-drive engines at the rear of the gunship.

Sponsorship emblem of Ado Eemon, ruler of Caramm V

Cooling radiator

Binocular range finder aids long-range spatial sense and missile guidance

Long-range sensor ports

Photoreceptor eye

Targeting scanners

Medium laser cannon

Laser cannon capacitor accumulates energy for blast

Medium laser cannon

Rotating mount of chin cannon

Movable mandibles

Inductors supply power to the turret across the ball-socket gap

Shield projector

Rangefinder pre-processor

Starboard deflector shield generator

Fuel tanks are exposed to reduce risk of radioactive fuel particles damaging vulnerable components under the hull

Portside targeting processor

Repulsor projector

Processor for sensors and antenna

Targeting sensor port

Independent, free rotation of turret cannons allows aggressive multi-targeting and compensates for low maneuverability

Super-compressed fusion reactant yields programmed blast

Thrust nozzle

Rocket reactor

Homing sensors

Flight processor

Fuel

Fins extend after launch

Controlled variable yield detonator

Power cell

Inertial compensator and tensor field generator protect components during turning accelerations over 10,000G

Air Support During the Separatist invasion of Kashyyyk in the Clone Wars, HMP droid gunships provide air support for NR-N99 tank droids.

DROID GUNSHIP

Ominous in appearance and relentless in battle, the droid gunship is a powerful, well-shielded missile platform. Designed for air strikes within planetary atmospheres, it moves at relatively slow speeds and possesses only average maneuverability, but this is compensated for by its awesome firepower. Two laser-cannon turrets can track targets independently, while torpedoes and missiles prove devastating against ground-based installations, attack vehicles, and fast short-range targets. The wing modules can carry extra laser cannons, concussion bombs, and upgraded targeting scanners. The droid gunship is truly a symbol of Separatist military might.

Waste gas vent

Reactor core

Power cell

Inner support frame

Repulsorlift generator

Ion drive thrusters are located in grooves on aft surface

Repulsor projector grid applies anti-gravitational lift when flying over a planet's surface

Exotic, superdense radioactive fuel supplied by Phlac-Arphocc Automata Industries, designers of the Confederacy fleet's fightercraft

Power convertor draws energy from cells for distribution to fighter's systems

Unfastened magnetic clamp

Fuel pump

Wing is removable at hinge

Light laser cannon

Pylon wing module supports heavy rocket ordnance

Concussion bomb is slower than regular rockets and unleashes over 600 times as much destructive energy

Homing sensor window

MODULAR WINGS

The droid gunship's wings can carry a range of interchangeable, mission-specific payloads. Dozens of missile and torpedo types can be deployed, tailored for special capabilities and effects. These include concentrated and wide-range blasts, electromagnetic pulses to wipe out the enemy's electrical systems, incendiary devices, and hard radiation bursts. Heavy concussion bombs are effective against larger ground-based targets, but are too cumbersome to hit fighters precisely. Additional wing-tip laser cannons can be fitted for long-range and line-of-sight engagements.

CONFEDERACY CORRUPTION

Mass-produced in Baktoid's factories on numerous Confederacy worlds, the droid gunship plays a vital role in the Separatist forces. On some of these planets, power-hungry despots keep a number of these vessels for their own personal use. Many gunships used in General Grievous's raid on Coruscant bear the triple-spiral sponsorship logo of Ado Eemon, the silken-tongued ruler of Caramm V. Eemon deploys his own personal fleet of gunships to ruthlessly eliminate all threats to his power, ravaging the once-beautiful world in the process.

JUGGERNAUT

Juggernaut! The very name of these rolling giants calls up memories of crushing defeat for the galaxy's quintillions of battle droids and their Separatist masters. Each of the Galactic Republic's HAVw A6 Juggernauts is a monstrous, ten-wheeled, armored box, built around a powerful reactor core and engine, with blasters and grenade launchers on every side. As well as being a front-line assault vehicle, these hulks provide secure shelter and transport for a company of dedicated clone troopers. Rugged and powerful, Juggernauts are the well-chosen backbone of the clone armies. Under the command of Jedi Master Yoda, they form the most integral part of a dogged campaign to eject battle droid invaders from the strategic Wookiee world of Kashyyyk.

ROLLING WAR-MACHINE

Although wheeled transport may seem like a graceless system from a prehistoric age, the large surface of the Juggernaut's wheels helps to reduce ground pressure, making the vehicle less prone to sinking in soft soil than heavy walkers. Direct ground contact also protects it from electromagnetic attacks and shield discharges, and it can stop and turn in a smaller radius than any repulsorlift craft. Nearly impenetrable armor and an arsenal of beam and missile weapons make the Juggernaut more than a match for most of the Separatists' ground-based war machines.

Rapid-repeating heavy laser cannon

Flip-down entry to smaller cockpit

Twin stairwell down to rear deployment hatch

Troop cabin life-support systems

Thermally superconducting armor absorbs enemy beams and spreads heat harmlessly over a wide area

Smaller cockpit

Surface scoring from hit by dwarf spider droid

Medium antipersonnel laser-cannon shaft extends from hull

Independent wheel suspension

Internal gearing of wheel segments

Main drive shaft runs along almost the full length within the undercarriage

Versatile wheel segments can spin at different rates

Reactor and engine systems

Troop Transport Nicknamed the "rolling slab," the Juggernaut's modifiable interior typically carries 50 troops and their gear, but can hold as many as 300.

DOUBLE-HEADED MONSTER

Each of a Juggernaut's wheels consists of three versatile, independently spinning segments, which enable the hulking vehicle to move smoothly across even the most inhospitable terrain. The vehicle can also reverse direction easily, moving equally well in forward and reverse gears. Either cockpit can assume full control, which has led to much debate among Juggernaut clone crews as to which cockpit is the true "front" end.

mpartmental
ast-door

Power trunk routes energy to
blaster cannon

ive gunnery
tations with
mmersive
olographic
elmet fire
ontrols

Upper heavy laser
cannon turret has best
all-round view

Troops sit eagerly
awaiting battle

Ladder
between
decks

Ladders to
upper troop
hatches

Spotter

Retractable
ladder rungs

Retractable rocket/
grenade launcher

Mast can
telescope up or
down when rungs
are retracted

Observation
post provides
greater visibility
than is possible
at hull height

FORMIDABLE BLASTING

Juggernauts are designed to deliver tremendous firepower in order
to overwhelm well-shielded military structures, some of which can
withstand a lone Juggernaut's barrage for hours. Against an unshielded
target, however, a Juggernaut can blast the equivalent heat of a
nuclear bomb into one small spot, creating a blazing fireball.

Ammunition loading
hatch splits into
separate halves for
partial cover

Spotlights

Clone casualties attended to by
2-1B medical droid

Large dome hatch covers
scanner gear

Communications dish

Clone
major

Safety blast-door separates
cockpit from other sections

Commanding officer's
observation hatch, often
occupied by a Jedi

Navigator

Pilots wear
lighter armor
for better
articulation
while seated

Twin antipersonnel
blaster cannons

Armored
transparisteel
viewport

Jaw lowers to reveal twin
blaster cannons

Left- and right-side gunners
compete over droid kill-scores

Powerful headlights scan terrain using
visible and invisible beams of light

Steering
pinion

AT-RT

The All Terrain Recon Transport (AT-RT) is an armed, mobile platform for a single soldier on a patrol or reconnaissance mission. These walkers support policing actions in dense civilian areas, and are also used in cooling battle zones. A lightweight body makes it faster than the rarer one-man AT-PT (All Terrain Personal Transport). Lacking an enclosed cabin, the driver enjoys a clear view, but is exposed to small-arms fire. The AT-RT's blaster cannon is devastating against infantry, but weak against the armor of tank, spider, and crab droids.

ELEVATED WARRIORS

With the AT-RT's elevated view and nose-mounted repeating laser, a clone pilot is able to spot and attack long-distance targets that might go unseen by allied foot soldiers. Pilots are trained to serve as lone scouts or work in teams, and a squad of four AT-RTs can easily overpower a single Trade Federation Armored Assault Tank (AAT). Hand-held controls, foot-pedals, and a posture-sensitive saddle serve as combined steering mechanisms for the AT-RT, and are designed to operate with intuitive ease. A motion-detection scanner as well as data displays for numerous sensors help the AT-RT pilot sight targets in various environments.

Enhanced helmet comlink

Comms antennae

Power cells

Exhaust baffles

Engine

Cooling vents

Steering controls

Terrain scanner

Control and navigation systems

Laser cannon

Coordination and posture controller

Laser cannon power unit

Trooper's divisional heraldic pattern denotes past battle honors under Jedi command

Shoulder suspension

Upper elbow actuator and suspension

Mid-leg actuators

Upper ankle

Cutting/ grappling claw

Night Patrol AT-RTs are equipped with headlights and floodlights that can be adjusted to cut through dense fog, snow, and dust.

COMMERCE GUILD SUPPORT DESTROYER

Separatist *Recusant*-class light destroyers are mass-produced by zealous workers led by Techno Union foremen, using materials from many Commerce Guild worlds. Since the beginning of the Clone Wars, countless numbers of these support vessels have been built, destroyed in battle, and replaced. Lone *Recusant*-class ships often carry out attacks on Loyalist commercial shipping, but their real effectiveness becomes apparent when deployed in large numbers. Four to six can outgun a Republic *Venator*-class or *Victory*-class Star Destroyer, although it would take 1,000 *Recusant*-class ships to take on Kuat Drive Yard's *Mandator-II* Star Dreadnaught.

Collision Alert Because most Commerce Guild light destroyers are crewed by droids without any sense of self-preservation, they rarely hesitate to deliberately ram Republic Star Destroyers.

Hyperdrive

Ionization chambers

Power connections between stern and reactors in main hull

Main reactor annihilates up to 8,600 tons of fuel per second

"Hollow" interior shelters Separatist fightercraft

Electromagnetic sensor antennae

Dual light laser cannon

Command bridge

Thruster nozzle

Habitable decks

Heavy turbolaser turrets

Internal transit shaft

Point-defense laser cannon

Neutrino radiator grille

Prow turbolaser cannon

Smooth hull segments guide circulating energy shields

Heavy turbolaser cannon

TACTICAL SIMPLICITY

Primarily controlled by droid technology, the *Recusant*-class light destroyer was based on technical schematics that Quarren Separatists stole from Mon Calamari designers. The destroyer's most significant feature is its strong armament, which includes heavy turbolasers in a fixed mount on the ship's prow. The destroyer's only weakness may be its droid brain's single-mindedness, as it is compelled to stubbornly attack a single target while ignoring all others until the target is destroyed or disabled.

Fuel tank

Feeder lines for
fire-retardants

Centrifugal
pump

Copilot
cockpit

Cowled jet
engine

Heat
exchanger

Repulsorlift
generator

Siren and
warning lights

Repulsorlift heat sinks

Tanks can carry
alternative powders
or liquids for dealing
with different types
of fires

Tank refiller cap

Repulsorlift projection
vanes

Tractor beam projector lifts disaster
victims up towards the vehicle

Shield
generator

Fire-retardant agents
mix as they exit nozzle
at high pressure

DAMAGE CONTROL

The battle over Coruscant has a disastrous impact on Galactic City. Each crashing battleship scars the cityscape with a ten-kilometer (six mile) crater and the shockwaves flatten buildings in the vicinity. Daring rescue-service pilots fly tirelessly in countless civic emergency vehicles, saving crews from doomed ships and guiding the falling hulks to minimize damage and loss of life. Firespeeders flock to spray-cool the plunging *Invisible Hand*'s flaming hull. Their invaluable assistance helps Anakin Skywalker to gain control of the wreck and make a relatively soft impact, saving the lives of thousands of innocent residents.

Deep interior space
containing vital reactors
and infrastructure is
maintained as a
zero-gravity space

Dorsal sensor and communications masts
coordinate nearby droid fighters. General
Grievous accesses this system via
comlinks built into his cybernetic systems,
directing Invisible Hand's defense

Proton torpedo
tube

Compressed
reactant tank

Major corridor is wide
enough to allow access
for IG-227 Hailfire droids

Dual laser
cannon
turret

Confederacy of
Independent
Systems emblem

Tractor beam
projectors

Internal
framework

Inertial
compensator

Dual laser cannon

Main hull is thicker and more
extensive than those found on most
small- and medium-sized Separatist
warships

Viewing portals are not
necessary for a ship with an
all-droid crew, but are
retained for the benefit of
occasional living passengers

Failed deflector shields
expose hull to heat of
atmospheric re-entry—
temperature will rise to
thousands of degrees

INVISIBLE HAND

In a bold strike at the galactic capital Coruscant, raiders from the Separatist flagship *Invisible Hand* have abducted Supreme Chancellor Palpatine. The vessel waits in orbit with the Confederacy fleet as the droid kidnappers return with their valuable prize—but before they can flee, thousands of Republic battleships engage the craft, trapping it in an upper atmospheric combat within the planet's defensive shield. *Invisible Hand* is badly damaged by enemy guns, so Jedi rescuers Obi-Wan Kenobi and Anakin Skywalker must find Palpatine in a rapidly decaying spacewreck. Ruptured compartments are flooded with fluidic coolants and propellants laced with invisible, exotic hypermatter fuels. Artificial gravity, tensor fields, and inertial compensators all begin to fail, as the crippled ship threatens to tear itself apart. The battle rages on, until *Invisible Hand* begins its meteoric fall toward the surface of Coruscant.

Fireship captain Jikesh Valia flies to the aid of the failing Separatist flagship

Medical bay door

Vertical access to upper deck

Fireman Pont Edisser readies his repulsorlift disk platform for flying rescues

Manuevering thruster

Antigravity life jackets

Spare hazard suits

Access hatch

Hyperdrive reactant silo

Chancellor Palpatine and the Jedi prisoners are brought to the bridge to face General Grievous as the ship begins its fiery descent toward Coruscant

Empty escape pod bays, jettisoned by General Grievous to spite his enemies

Powerful deflector shield generator network

Invisible Hand *is under the overall control of General Grievous, commander of the Confederacy's droid armies*

Corridor

Reactors can annihilate up to 12,000 tons of fuel per second

Command bridge

Subsidiary reactor

Transverse bulkhead

BANKING CLAN FRIGATE

The Banking Clan's *Munificent*-class star frigates are combat-communication ships, which assist with the navigation and coordination of Separatist fleets deep in hostile space. Powerful antennae channel hyperwave supralight transceivers, while jamming devices hinder enemy sensors and targeting systems. Two huge turbolaser cannons can blast-melt an ice-moon measuring 1,000 kilometers (621 miles) in diameter, or pierce the shields of a 10 km-wide (6.2 mile-wide) Grade III battle station. These ships once guarded banker's vaults on Outer Rim worlds and menaced planets heavily in debt to the Banking Clan. Now they escort and coordinate Separatist fleet actions, such as attacks on the interstellar HoloNet relays, which consequently blind and isolate Loyalist forces.

The Munificent-class frigate's hull extends over and below its seven ion drive thrusters, providing a physical shield to the thrusters from all angles except directly behind

Ray shield generator dissipates harmful energy blasts

Active neutrino radiator and shield heat-sinks

Ion drive thruster

Energy cells

Long-range hyperwave transceiver mast can establish communications links anywhere in the galaxy

Power feeds

Hyperdrive units

Power trunk

Main reactors together annihilate up to 2,300 tons of fuel per second

Power feeds

Hull armor covers critical parts

Superdense reactant tanks

Docking ring

Sensory antennae and point-defense guns

Impact mark left by the collision of the late Jedi Master Wom-Nii Gnaden in his NTB-630 bomber, during the Battle of Crombach Nebula

Emblem of Confederacy of Independent Systems combined-volunteer forces

Twin turbolaser turret

Fatal Hit High in Coruscant's orbit, a *Munificent*-class frigate is wracked by a massive explosion caused by enemy fire.

Frigate Bridge Prior to the Clone Wars, the *Munificent*-class frigate's spacious, multi-leveled bridge accommodated a Muun crew, and housed utilitarian cabins as well as suites and observation decks for wealthy Banking Clan administrators and dignitaries. The frigate is now crewed entirely by Separatist droids.

SEPARATIST SHIPS

While vast campaigns detain millions of Separatist warships in the Outer Rim, a few dozen battleships lead thousands of destroyers and frigates in a bold strike on the galactic capital Coruscant. These light warships, bristling with small laser turrets and impressive, oversized cannons, were pledged to Count Dooku by the governments of hundreds of aggressively independent star sectors. As the craft are largely controlled by automated droid-brain technology, little crew space is required. This gives the ships a sinister, skeletal appearance. Destroyers and frigates are not equipped with hangars or ground-attack armies but carry enough security droids for boarding actions. Their hull cavities can also "host" Separatist droid starfighters.

Power cells

Twin main reactors can run alone if one is damaged

Light turbolaser turrets

Frigate monitors a fleet's perimeters using high-performance sensors with a range of several light-days

Turbolift shaft

Command bridge

Forward scanner

Inertial compensator and tensor fields that maintain structural integrity run along the longitudinal spines

Ion cannon

Semi-exposed frame

Front starboard power trunk

Prow turbolaser elevation mount

Habitable areas with droid crews and troops

Former storage vaults for galactic currencies and precious metals are now used to transport military hardware

Powerful forward laser cannon is slow to maneuver but deadly to larger warships

Expansive windows provide 180-degree view

Observation deck

Interstellar communications array

Internal freight shaft and engineering access

Point-defense laser cannons

Auxiliary reactor

Refitted communications and sensor pod

Turbolift shaft

Conning tower

Droid Vulture fighters prowl the stricken ship's surface, ready to attack any approaching Loyalist fightercraft

Portside hyperdrive module

WIZARD'S TOWER

Shortly before the Coruscant strike, *Invisible Hand's* main communications and sensor pod was refitted as a lofty sanctum for Count Dooku, the political leader of the Separatist cause. Sith cunning and Jedi wisdom make Dooku a peerless exponent of manipulative propaganda—he affects a simple and saintly image and is called "Gentle Hand" by superstitious folk on innumerable worlds. From the ship's tower, Dooku transmits spiritualistic appeals to agitate and divide the galactic populace. Unless he is stopped, the Sith Lord will broadcast the holo-image of the captive Supreme Chancellor Palpatine around the galaxy to crush Loyalist morale.

Deck Cannons The Separatist flagship is armed with mass driver cannons—projectile weapons that rest on deck-mounted swivel platforms. Unlike turbolasers, the cannons have an ammunition feed and release expended shells when fired.

Shielded thrusters deflect ion particle streams to generate reverse braking thrust

Plasma leak from engine

INFAMOUS TRICKS

Under the command of the bloodthirsty General Grievous, *Invisible Hand* has played a key role in many of the Separatist cyborg's most notorious forays into the Galactic Core. These include the release of the Loedorvian Brain Plague that slew Republic clone armies and nearly every human in the Weemell Sector. The ship was also used to supervise naval attacks on 26 strategic Loyalist worlds. These included the hour-long orbital bombardment that depopulated and melted the crust of the former city-planet of Humbarine, an ancient founding world of the Republic. Loyalist agents have tried to track the vessel's movements, but Grievous frequently swaps Mid Rim patrols with her sister ship *Lucid Voice* to confuse the enemy.

Hangar entrance's atmospheric shield projector is wrecked by Anakin Skywalker's attack in his Jedi Interceptor

Access to engine and power generator area

A WOUNDED BEAST

Invisible Hand attempts to drift inconspicuously in the concentrated shelter of Separatist battleships, destroyers, and frigates. Large numbers of droid Vulture fighters and tri-fighters cluster protectively around the flagship. When Kenobi and Skywalker approach in their Jedi Interceptors, the ship's deflector shields are already failing—small areas of the hull are open to attack from even the tiniest fighters. Anakin shoots out the atmosphere containment shield protecting the hangar entry, breaching the vessel's defenses.

Command Bridge Captured by Separatist droid soldiers, Obi-Wan Kenobi, Anakin Skywalker, and Supreme Chancellor Palpatine are escorted to *Invisible Hand*'s command bridge.

Droid-crewed maintenance decks

Separatist MTT (Multi-Troop Transport)

Ground forces command section

Anakin Skywalker's Jedi Interceptor

Thrusters and reactors usually fill the stern of Providence-class ships—Invisible Hand's expansive hangars are a major design modification

Air ducts—minimal atmospheric circulation is required as Invisible Hand carries few living crew or passengers

Ceiling racks typically hold 120 droid tri-fighters and Vulture fighters

Heavy damage received during encounter with Republic Star Destroyer Guarlara

Emergency airbrake panels increase resistance slightly

Mass driver deck cannons

The stresses of atmospheric entry and loss of internal tensor fields will cause ship to break up near this area

Curved panelling is typical of flowing design style of Invisible Hand's Quarren shipbuilders

Segment of hangar's blast door ready to shut

Quad turbolaser cannon's maximum yield is equivalent to magnitude-10 earthquake

Heavy lift platform

Claw-like hangar crane

Stored ground vehicles include 160 MTTs (Multi-Troop Transports) plus 280 other vehicles including AATs (Armored Assault Tanks), Hailfire droids, OG-9 spider droids and LM-432 crab droids

UTAPAUN P-38 FIGHTER

The remote planet Utapau, located in the Tarabba Sector, relies on the Porax-38 (P-38) starfighter for defensive and offensive engagements. These tough, hyperdrive-equipped fightercraft have versatile thrusters, dual-reactor systems, high-capacity deflector shielding, and long-distance sensor systems that provide early warning of enemy activity. When Tion Medon, the Master of Utapau Port Administration, realizes General Grievous's Separatist forces are about to land on Utapau, he orders his outgunned P-38 forces into hiding. However, with General Kenobi's arrival and the hope of Loyalist military intervention, Medon recalls his pilots in a frantic, fiery bid for freedom.

Thruster branch vents direct thrust up or down for pitch maneuvers

Starboard thruster nozzle

High-capacity heat exchanger cools engine

Ion accelerator

Power distributor draws and stores energy from wing reactor and regulates power to nearby components

Small navicomputer can be loaded with charts for local sector only

Hyperdrive motivator

Headrest

Life support systems

Heat-sink cells for deflector shields

Each wing reactor annihilates up to 3.1 kg of fuel per second

Deflector shield projector web

Fuel injector manifold

Fuel tank

Capacitors accumulate power to energize laser cannon

Symmetrical power feeds deliver energy burst

Repulsor cells

Resonance and beam-amplification chamber

Inertial compensator band

Tibanna coolant recycler feeds

Anti-static spikes

High-power laser cannon

Links between starboard comm/scan systems

Forward scanners

Organic Construction Massive fossilized bones from giant creatures are repurposed as load-bearing beams on landing pads for P-38 fighters.

HOME FORCE

The Trade Federation protects its position in remote galactic regions by placing embargoes on arms sales to planetary governments. As a result, Utapauns rely upon self-made, downscaled ships—their biggest anti-pirate Rendili Dreadnaught is one-fifth of the size of a Trade Federation battleship. Lacking a heavy navy, Utapauns deploy a rugged and potent starfighter force. Their large P-38 fighters are capable of independent hyperspace jumps, which enables them to defend the security of Utapau far into the Tarabba Sector. The interstellar range of these ships means they can endure longer, more arduous missions than tiny, fleet-based craft such as Separatist droid fighters, Republic V-wings, and Jedi starfighters.

The Utai Since the Separatist invasion, the diminutive Utai workers in Pau city have had to work on their hidden P-38 fighters in secret.

Utai Air Commodore Senin Vant leads the bi-species Utapau Skyforce

Breath mask and comlink

"Sepulchral Ruby" heraldic motif

Rangefinder/targeting processor

Jamming device

Data buffers

Active scanner power supply

Stable low-noise scanners cooled with liquid helium

Flight instruments

Airspeed sensors

Smear and dent from impact of Utapaun flying squid

Power feeds from portside reactor

Transparisteel canopy

Footrest

Inertial compensator applies force fields to counter acceleration stresses

Windswept World The winds in Utapau's atmosphere are so strong that Utapaun pilots often spend more time beneath the surface than in the air.

RECLAIMING UTAPAU

Utapauns live on an eerie world of wind, bones, and caves far from Tarabba Prime, the nearest major shipping and communications hub. The planet is shared by two humanoid species, the Utai and the Pau'ans, known collectively as Utapauns. Utapau's only asset is its obscurity, which General Grievous exploits to keep his new headquarters a secret from Republic forces. When the Utapauns decide to fight back against the Separatist occupation, local knowledge and the P-38's advanced scanner systems give them a sharp advantage in high-speed chases through the treacherous canyon terrain. Powerful jammers also prove surprisingly effective at interfering with Separatist droid control signals. Any droids within targeting range are isolated, and must rely on their low-intelligence individual droid-brains.

TECHNO UNION SHIPS

The Techno Union is the galaxy's foremost developer of emerging technologies, including advanced engineering and microelectronics. Strongly devoted to the Separatist agenda, the Techno Union incorporates technology from such cutting-edge corporations as Haor Chall Engineering, Republic Sienar Systems, Kuat Systems Engineering, TaggeCo, and Feethan Ottraw Scalable Assemblies. Feethan Ottraw's contribution to the Techno Union's cause includes the Mankvim-814 light interceptor, Belbullab-23 heavy assault craft, and Belbullab-22 heavy starfighter. Unlike Vulture droids and droid tri-fighters, Belbullab-22s are powerful enough go one-on-one with the Republic's ARC-170 starfighters.

Rapid Retreat When Republic warships arrive on Geonosis, the Techno Union's *Hardcell*-class transports prepare for an emergency evacuation.

- Deflector shield generator
- Cockpit hinge
- Canopy
- Sensory processor
- Ion acceleration chamber
- Fuel tank
- Ion drive thruster nozzle
- Articulation frame for thruster rudder
- Magnetized thrust-vectoring rudder
- Side thrusters
- Ionization chamber
- Wing shoulder joint
- Forward scanner
- Repulsorlift generator
- Wing provides some aerodynamic lift in subsonic atmospheric flight

INTERSTELLAR TRANSPORT

The signature transport for Techno Union officials is the *Hardcell*-class interstellar transport, which features six large, powerful thrusters that wreak havoc on launch sites but enable quick exits from planetary atmospheres. Because the Techno Union was founded and remains largely operated by Skakoans, most *Hardcell*-class transports have pressurized cabins engineered specifically for Skakoan biology, allowing them to forego their bulky pressure suits while traveling. Before the Clone Wars began, the Techno Union contributed nearly 300 *Hardcell*-class transports to the Separatist cause. Of those transports, 117 failed to escape the Battle of Geonosis.

MANKVIM-814 LIGHT INTERCEPTOR

Numerous Mankvim-814 interceptors flock to defend the Separatist foothold on Utapau. The Techno Union built these small, short-range starfighters on the planet from local materials, having hastily constructed factories in the ancient Grand Halls with no regard for Utapau's architectural heritage. The Mankvim's simple construction centers on a reactor feeding power and plasma to a high-velocity ion-drive. A magnetized rudder tilts the ion flow for off-axis thrust, while smaller side thrusters aid roll and yaw adjustments. The craft is equipped with twin rapid-fire laser cannons and durable shields for combat. Aerodynamic wings fitted with repulsorlifts also aid overall maneuverability.

Weak Spot Although it can deploy hundreds of battle droids, the *Hardcell*-class transport is only lightly armed, and vulnerable to well-placed shots to the area above the fuel cells, which can destroy the entire transport.

GRIEVOUS'S STARFIGHTER

Although he prefers hand-to-hand combat, General Grievous often flies a battle-worn Belbullab-22 starfighter designed by Feethan Ottraw Scalable Assemblies, specialists in self-constructing armaments factories. Made for a living pilot, the hyperdrive-equipped craft is bulkier and hardier than disposable droid fighters. Two main ion drives enable the Belbullab to keep pace with an Utapaun P-38 fighter. A rear-mounted thrust-vectoring fin and auxiliary thrusters built into the wings assist with yaw and roll maneuvers. Rapid-firing triple laser cannons sustain firepower of equivalent destructive force to that of the Loyalists' V-wing starfighters.

Landing Pad Battle Obi-Wan Kenobi fights to stop the Confederacy's General Grievous from escaping in his Belbullab-22 fighter on Utapau.

Triple laser cannon

Power convertor

Hyperdrive

Flight instruments and navicomputer

Shield generator

Thrust vectoring fin

Portside main thruster

Life support systems

Gray impervium hull coating similar to armor worn by Republic clone troops

Auxiliary thrusters

Lateral thrust ducts

Ion accelerator chamber

Forward scanner

GETAWAY VEHICLE

To maintain contact with his droid armies, General Grievous's starfighter, *Souless One*, has a sophisticated compact HoloNet transceiver. The transceiver can also access Republic and pirate networks, allowing Grievous to anticipate enemy activity and avoid confrontations he can't win. After Republic forces arrive on Utapau, Grievous attempts to escape in his starfighter, which he keeps on a secret landing pad. Unknown to Grievous, his previous use of the starfighter to retreat from battle has prompted some enemies to nickname his fighter *Spineless One*.

Cockpit Layout Like the controls of General Grievous's Wheel Bike, the Belbullab-22's cockpit features a circular, pressure-sensitive panel for operating the ship. Set within a reinforced yoke, the controls can be operated by most humanoids.

GRIEVOUS'S WHEEL BIKE

General Grievous's fearsome reputation as a merciless military leader is reinforced by a personal fleet of specialized killing machines and vehicles. On cavernous Utapau, the cyborg General drives a wheel bike—a tumbling twin-wheel that surrounds a central motor. Grievous's military vehicle is an offshoot of the Banking Clan's hoop-wheeled Hailfire droids, designed to roll at intimidating speed on hard surfaces. It can also raise itself up on two pairs of legs to walk over the top of battle wrecks and other obstacles. A double laser cannon replaces one side seat, and Grievous can wield either a conveniently placed electrostaff, a blaster, or one of his Jedi lightsaber trophies when he rolls into battle. Flexing claws skirt the wheels to provide a smoother ride, or clutch the ground as climbing teeth.

Knuckle joint of rim claw

Outer drive chain

Side claw

Console graphic display is adjusted to suit the color perception of Grievous's species' eyesight

Claw pivot

Laser cannon's beam-resonance chamber

Cannon elevation motor

Capacitors store charge for laser cannon shots

Anti-static spikes

Double laser cannon

Waste coolant gas discharge vents

Claw actuators

Dense and massive drive chain spins within outer wheel, providing gyro stability

Frictionless magnetic rail

Transformation and accelerator controls

Control wiring

Magnetic disk brake

Teeth of left driver wheel

Driver's footrest

Control Panel The bike's directional controls are housed in an illuminated, touch-sensitive console, reinforced so it won't shatter under the pressure of Grievous's sharp metal fingers.

NEW HEADQUARTERS

General Grievous's invading forces have constructed command centers and self-replicating Techno Union factories on Utapau. These facilities create new troops, starfighters, wheel bikes, and other vehicles using local materials. If left undisturbed, they will turn Utapau into yet another of the Outer Rim's fortress worlds, riddled with ugly refineries and assembly lines and trembling under the weight of ever-more deadly Separatist war machines.

ROLLER RACING

Grievous's wheel bike is put to the test when General Kenobi, astride the lizard-like varactyl Boga, pursues the cyborg on a dangerous chase through the windmills and chasms of Pau city. As the Separatist general speeds toward his escape ship, the deadly wheel bike smashes over or through many obstacles. The hoop-wheels derive their stability from the gyroscopic effect of massive, counterspinning internal chains. The individual links that make up the chains incorporate built-in capacitors, which store reserve energy to power the legs and blaster when the engine is idle.

Precarious Pursuit The wheel bike's strong grip gives it incredible agility, as discovered by Obi-Wan when he chases Grievous through the canyons of Utapau.

Armored plating

Grievous's skull antennae enable him to control his battle droid forces by radio command

Gripping claws of left foot

Tail guard and exhaust vents

Inner rim frame

Sockets engage teeth of drive wheel

Lightsaber blade is a delicately tuned, massless standing wave of energy

Grievous's robotic arms can split in two, enabling him to drive and fight at the same time

Foot claws

Lightsaber won from slain Jedi Master Jmmaar, a 10- legged, crablike being from the planet Vvaw

Unnecessary soft padding has been removed from seat and replaced with magnetic panels to secure General Grievous's metallic body to the vehicle

Armored chestplate covers Grievous's few remaining humanoid organs

Leg actuator pneumatics

Climbing spur

Shin of left foreleg

Engine housing

Steering bars

119

WOOKIEE CATAMARAN

Wookiee *Oevvaor* catamarans are slim, twin-hulled craft that skid over the waters of Kashyyyk at breakneck speeds. They are lifted by a repulsorlift array up to a maximum height of 1,000 meters, propelled by Podracer-style jet engines or propeller pods, and steered by knife-like keels and rudders. Wookiee catamarans are normally used as fishing or sports craft, and are not equipped with built-in heavy weapons. But when Kashyyyk is invaded, hundreds of these craft are conscripted to bear Wookiee troops in small-arms attacks, darting through the lines of Separatist vehicles. The catamarans' speed and maneuverability are crucial, as Kashyyyk's defenders know that the enemy must first capture the coasts before attempting incursions into the tangled, dense vegetation of the inland woods.

Elderly Attichitcuk has practiced his throw in virtual-reality games played on an addictive Wookiee "mind evaporator" headset

High-velocity exhaust

Pitch control compensator

Adjustable length and weight

Heating elements liquefy fuel

Exhaust vent

Fuel in tank is solid at normal temperatures

Power generator

Rudder actuator

Side rudder

AGILE DEFENDERS

The Wookiee watercraft used in the defence of Kashyyyk are named after the Oevvaor, a predatory marine reptile of the Kashyyyk coasts known for its agility and territorial ferocity. The tough hulls of these aptly named catamarans are handcrafted from wroshyr timber. This light, strong, and durable wood is hewn from Kashyyyk's fabled wroshyr trees, which can grow to hundreds of meters in height.

Lower rudders dip into water when flying at sea level

Air Patrol Soaring over the lagoons and fjords of the Wawaatt Archipelago on Kashyyyk, a Wookiee catamaran angles toward the coastal tree-city of Kachirho.

Thermal detonator is a
miniature nuclear device

Prow resembles the axe-like horn
on the head of a male Oevvaor

Copilot Chewbacca spent many years
as a Claatuvac hyperspace route-
planner. His extensive knowledge of
trade routes make him a first-class
starship navigator

Wookiee vision is less
sharp than their sense
of smell, so they use
easy-to-read screen
graphics

Tactical
tracker

Upper
airscoop

Multi-stage
compressor

Annular
combustion
chamber

Pressure
release
vents

Fuel lines

Afterburner

Igniter

Nozzle

Power
cabling

Wookiee Ornithopter Built by the Appazanna Engineering Works, the same
manufacturer as the Wookiee catamaran, the *Raddaugh Gnasp* fluttercraft
takes its name from large, wasp-like insects native to Kashyyyk's moon Alaris.

Wide-angle
passive sensors

Directional
scanner

Air-intake
regulators

Compressor
fan rotator
shaft

Screen

The pilot, Sgt.
Zittaasabba, is
also an expert in
unarmed combat

Rudder yokes

Running boards

Handgrip

Gunner armed with
heavy blaster

Antigravity
generator

Repulsorlift
field vanes

High-powered
blaster beam

Wookiee blaster rifle is too
heavy for a human to carry
but fires ferocious bursts

Aerodynamic, streamlined
curves help ensure smooth,
stable flight

Sturdy wooden frame
provides the strength of
a towering wroshyr tree

STRATEGIC WORLD

Kashyyyk, or "Wookiee Planet C" as some humans call it, has long played a major
role in transgalactic shipping and communications. For centuries, an elite guild of
long-lived Wookiee cartographers known as the Claatuvac have maintained and
updated the hyperspace route surveys that keep the galaxy navigable. It is widely
believed that the Claatuvac Guild's ancient data archives contain many near-mythical,
long-lost routes that do not feature on official Republic charts. Conquering Kashyyyk
would enable the Separatists to control hyperspace route planning and to use the
Wookiees' secret routes to frustrate and monopolize galactic trade and communications.

HISTORY OF HOSTILITY

For 20 years, the Wookiees of Kashyyyk and its colony worlds have repeatedly
repelled encroachments by the greedy Trade Federation. In this new period of
unrestrained war, Confederacy invaders now bypass the colonies and attempt a
conclusive strike on the Wookiee homeworld. Although the Separatist invasion
fleet is driven off by General Yoda's Republic taskforce, a huge army of tank droids,
crab droids, and flying gunships occupies the tropical Wawaatt Archipelago. The
Wookiees know that they must marshal all their brawn, defensive weaponry, and
vehicular power to halt the intruders' advance.

SWAMP SPEEDER

The Grand Army of the Republic bolsters the Wookiees' defensive forces with a wide variety of imported war machines. The light, two-man ISP (Infantry Support Platform) speeder is the clone troops' closest equivalent of the Wookiees' *Oevvaor* catamarans and *Raddadugh Gnasp* fluttercraft. The clone army's antigravity repulsorlift vehicle floats smoothly in the air without touching land or water. It is driven by a powerful turbofan, which can be reversed to fire a braking airblast when needed. Precise, controlled vectoring of the turbofan's thrust makes the ISP a highly maneuverable attack vehicle. The front-mounted pair of twin-blaster cannons are lethal to enemy infantry, but can also prove highly effective against shielded enemy gunships, fighters, and Corporate Alliance NR-N99 tank droids.

UNIQUE TURBOFAN

Developed by Aratech Repulsor Company, and intended as a heavier version of the Republic Army's Biker Advanced Recon Commando (BARC) speeder, the ISP has a a rear-mounted turbofan that can generate a thrust of up to 100 kilometers per hour, and can be reverse vectored in emergencies to provide a sudden stop. The turbofan produces less noise than most ion thrusters.

Airflow vectoring fin

100 kph (62 mph) thrust fan

Control console

Seat belt

Forward-terrain laser scanner

Mudshield

Chassis

Repulsorlift

Blaster pre-charge capacitor

Swivelling twin-blaster cannons

ISPs on Felucia Introduced late in the Clone Wars, the ISP fulfills the Republic's need for a large mobile weapons platform that can travel over soft, waterlogged terrain. The ISP is deployed in the fungus forests of the planet Felucia, as well as on Kashyyyk.

FIT FOR AN EMPEROR

The Emperor's personal *Theta*-class shuttle serves as a mobile base from which he can further his goal of galactic domination. Separatist leaders, corrupt Senators, and other influential figures have been bribed, coerced, or threatened in the ship's secure aft compartment, while Sith truth potions, mind-control enhancers, torture devices, and memory erasers have all assisted Palpatine in his "negotiations."

Voyage into Darkness
Mystical Sith equipment capable of channeling the dark side of the Force helps sustain Darth Vader during the trip from Mustafar to a secret medical center on Coruscant.

FLIGHT MODE

Shields active, broadly spread, and centered around fuselage

Wings open

LANDING IN SAFETY

When the *Theta*-class shuttle lands, its long wings fold upwards to allow access via the main hatch. The ion drive powers down as antigravity repulsorlifts guide the ship to a gentle touchdown. Scanners linked to the computer-controlled weapons systems survey the landing site as the ship descends, ready to instantly eliminate any threat to the ship or its occupants.

DESCENT MODE

Folded wings concentrate shield energy around the shuttle's hull as it descends

Repulsorlift engaged

LANDING MODE

Engines and shields deactivated

Automated weapons systems active

Weight balanced along stable, widely spaced landing skids

PALPATINE'S SHUTTLE

Assassination and abduction have punctuated every stage of the Clone Wars, and a galactic leader such as the newly self-appointed Emperor Palpatine requires a secure personal transport. The new *Theta*-class T-2c shuttle is designed to ferry important officers, senators, and courtiers between planets and ships in safety. Capable of outgunning most starfighters, the ship is fitted with twin forward-mounted quad laser cannons and a single, high-powered tail gun. This destructive arsenal can be computer-controlled or manually operated from a combined communications and gunnery station in the cockpit. The long folding wings are designed to project powerful shielding fields, and they also aid stability during atmospheric flight.

Static discharge devices

Landing light

Raised boarding ramp

Communications transponders

Airlock door

Navicomputer

Prepared for combat, the pilot wears a full flight suit

Gunner/ communications stations

Power feeds inside leading edge are kept apart by heat-sink elements

Repulsorlift generator

High-power portside quad laser cannon

Extreme Shield Power Descending to the volcanic planet Mustafar, Palpatine's shuttle is protected from the intense heat and incendiary ash by energy shields that far exceed military standards.

ELITE TRANSPORT

Emperor Palpatine's shuttle has been upgraded by "Warthan's Wizards," the finest starship technicians in the galaxy. To provide instant transgalactic communications, they installed a hyperwave reflector akin to the secret homing devices of the Jedi Order. The shuttle is also lined with sensor masks that make the interior appear empty on conventional scanners. Palpatine's later shuttles will feature a cloaking device—making them invisible to all forms of light, gravity, and other known energies.

IMPERIAL SYMBOL

In the formative years of the Galactic Empire, Cygnus Spaceworks will lose the contract for its shuttle line to Sienar Fleet Systems. Key designers at Cygnus, lured by vast salaries, personal galactic yachts, and a cut of future profits, will defect to Sienar, taking their designs with them. In years to come, the configuration of the *Theta*-class and its descendants will become a symbol of Imperial prestige. Sienar will also produce the Empire's primary space-superiority craft, the TIE (Twin Ion Engine) fighter, as well as downscaled warships built to patrol remote sectors.

Dorsal shield generator boosts the ray-shield energy fields circulating between the upper and side wings

Main reactor and its hyperdense fuel are centered over the landing legs, for stability

Rear-mounted automated laser cannon

Secure overhead stowage compartment contains Sith artifacts, field equipment, and interrogation devices

Power feeds to aft, side and ventral systems

Hyperdrive module

Ion drive thruster nozzle focuses and ejects tenuous plasma at near-light speed

Ion accelerator in shoulder impels high-velocity thrust streams to stern

Emperor's Guard

FX-series emergency medical droid tends his patient with brisk efficiency

Lord Vader lies maimed, burned, and crippled after falling into volcanic ash during his duel with Obi-Wan Kenobi on Mustafar

Emperor Palpatine ponders the future of his new apprentice, the prophesied Chosen One of Jedi lore

Laser cannon power cells

Starboard shield generator

Wing frame

Small-scale thermal and neutrino radiator continually removes heat absorbed by shields

Enormous capacity heat-sinks beneath radiator take energy surges from shields

Miniature steering jets line the edge of the trailing wing

Minor shield heat sink and radiator unit

ORDERED IN ADVANCE

During his appointment as Supreme Chancellor of the Republic, Palpatine was already having his personal *Theta*-class T-2c shuttle modified to suit his anticipated requirements as Emperor. Although the shuttle is designed for a crew of five, automated weapons systems allow a single pilot to operate the vessel without any gunners.

YODA'S ESCAPE PODS

An escape pod is designed to carry a living being away from danger as quickly as possible. These basic craft roar and shake through the air, propelled by simple ion engines, while the occupant's ride is smoothed by inertial compensators and anti-gravity fields. In his escape from the forces of Emperor Palpatine's newly formed Galactic Empire, Jedi Master Yoda resorts to these devices twice in one week. Yoda's first pod is a simple, Wookiee-made vessel that lifts him away from danger on Kashyyyk. His second craft, which carries him into exile on Dagobah, is a larger, more sophisticated lander from Polis Massa, with advanced guidance systems and landing mechanisms.

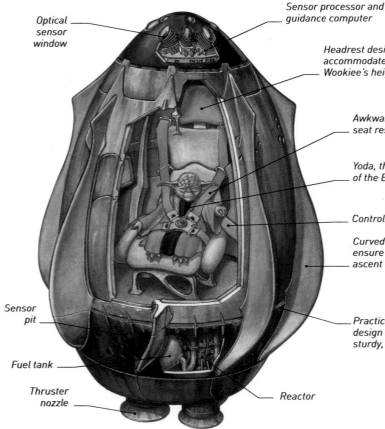

Optical sensor window

Sensor processor and guidance computer

Headrest designed to accommodate a Wookiee's height

Awkwardly-adjusted seat restraint

Yoda, the fugitive victor of the Battle of Kashyyyk

Control panel

Curved stabiliser fins ensure a stable, rifled ascent through the air

Sensor pit

Fuel tank

Thruster nozzle

Reactor

Practical Wookiee design reflected in sturdy, heatproof hull

Adjustable footpad

Reactor/ionization chamber

Fuel tanks are almost empty of reactant and propellant

Leg articulation socket

Fuel lines

Distress beacon, already deactivated by Yoda

Rations and survival gear

Seats designed for average male Massan

ESCAPE FROM KASHYYYK

With Separatist droids invading parts of Kashyyyk, Wookiee defenders prepared thousands of hidden escape pods for last-resort evacuation. General Yoda used the first pod. Its three sublight thrusters—cobbled together from three shipwrecks—contain just enough fuel to bear him safely into interplanetary space. Yoda deactivates its tell-tale distress beacon, relying solely on his Jedi pocket emergency transmitter. Alderaanian agents searching for surviving Jedi intercept Yoda's call, leading Senator Bail Organa to rescue him.

A HIDDEN SANCTUARY

After discovering the disappearance of the planet Kamino from Jedi navigational charts at the beginning of the Clone Wars, Yoda discreetly scanned for other gaps. Throughout the entire galaxy, he detected 37 more "missing" star systems. Some hid amazing strategic resources, while on others he met fiendish foes. With the dark side of the Force ever more pervasive, Yoda chose to keep one lost planet, Dagobah, as his private secret. In so doing, he was able to outwit the phantom menace responsible for deleting the Jedi files. By adopting Dagobah as his hiding place, Yoda now awaits a new hope for the galaxy in safe, if lonely, isolation.

Casing rings of thrusters will be cannibalised for use in Yoda's dwelling

Electrostatic nozzle

Plasma feeds

Engine's maximum thrust is 300G, slow even for a civilian ship

n acceleration chamber

Startup power cell

Power cabling

DERELICT TRANSPORT

Following Padmé's funeral on Naboo, Yoda secretly accompanies the Polis Massan attendees back to their world. There, he stows away on a freighter carrying supplies to the Separatist stronghold Sluis Van. As the ship briefly drops out of hyperspace just outside Dagobah, Yoda launches his escape pod, undetected, to begin his exile. With no hyperdrive for a return journey, Yoda fashions the pod into a crude dwelling; the hull plates form floor foundations and thruster rings make window and door frames.

Armored hull plates will be used in Yoda's hut

Pneumatic ram

Foot articulation linkage

Electromagnetic clamp locks sliding elements

Terrain telemetry processor aids balance and touchdown

Restraint /tractor field elements hold occupant

Inertial compensators screen pod interior from effects of violent accelerations

Landing repulsorlift elements

Scorch marks from atmospheric entry

Flight control

Leg pivot

Sensory processors

Main forward scanner

Hatch hinge

Hatch edge locks magnetically into frame

Egress hatch

Illuminated steps ensure visibility after a landing in dark conditions

Night Launch After evading Republic clone troops that have mysteriously turned against him, Yoda slips away from Kashyyyk in a Wookiee-made evacuation pod.

EPISODES IV–VI

A NEW HOPE
THE EMPIRE STRIKES BACK
RETURN OF THE JEDI

After two decades of oppressive rule, the Empire's hold on the galaxy is thoroughly entrenched. Anakin Skywalker has become Darth Vader, Emperor Palpatine's Sith Lord apprentice and enforcer. Vader is dedicated to crushing the Rebel Alliance—an organization that seeks to overthrow the Empire and restore the Galactic Republic. Anakin and Padmé's children, who were separated at birth to protect them from the Emperor, are now thrown together by fate. Unaware of their true parentage, the siblings—Tatooine farm boy Luke Skywalker and Princess Leia Organa of Alderaan—lead the Rebellion to a crucial victory with the destruction of the first Death Star battle station. While Luke trains to become a Jedi under the ancient Jedi Master Yoda, the Empire retaliates and the Rebellion is severely weakened. But the Alliance regroups and a decisive final battle results in both the destruction of the second Death Star and the redemption of Anakin Skywalker, who ultimately rejects the dark side of the Force and destroys the Emperor.

BLOCKADE RUNNER

Princess Leia Organa of Alderaan travels far and wide on board her consular starship *Tantive IV*, negotiating peace settlements and bringing aid to imperiled populations. Commanded by the daring and loyal Captain Antilles, Leia's *Tantive IV* is a Corellian Corvette: an older, hand-crafted ship of a make seen throughout the galaxy. Owned by the Royal House of Alderaan, this versatile craft has served two generations of Alderaanian Senators since it was first acquired by Leia's father, Bail Organa, as his personal transport. Under the cover of diplomatic immunity, the *Tantive IV* has carried out a range of missions for the Rebel Alliance, making its added armor plate as vital as its formal state conference chamber. This sturdy ship has brought the Organas through many harrowing adventures, and it is only under the pursuit of Darth Vader that the *Tantive IV* is finally overtaken and captured.

> ## "If this is a consular ship, where is the Ambassador?"
> ### Darth Vader

High-capacity pod is boarded via central access ladder

Armed high-capacity escape pod doubles as long-range laser turret

Leia's stateroom suite

Added armor plate permanently covers stateroom windows

Formal dining room

Control and power linkages

Mid-ship elevator

Forward elevator

Officers' briefing room

Officers' quarters

Computer power substation

Formal state conference chamber

Leia's seat

Tech station monitors ship operations

Darth Vader throttles Captain Antilles

Cockpit

Operations forum

Escape pod access tunnel

Rebel prisoners and droids being escorted off the ship for interrogation

Commander Praji in main computer room

Captain Antilles' quarters

Forward airlock docking hatch

Defensive field projector

Lower turbolaser is manned by two gunners

Escape pod that C-3PO and R2-D2 will use

ESCAPE PODS

Spacecraft escape pods range from coffin-like capsules to large lifeboats that are small ships in their own right. The Blockade Runner carries eight small escape pods rated for up to three people, and four laser-armed pods that seat 12. More sophisticated than the smaller pods, these lifeboats nonetheless have a very limited range. None of the *Tantive IV*'s escape systems could save its crew from the *Devastator*'s guns.

No Escape The heavily damaged *Tantive IV* is pulled into the main hangar of the Imperial Star Destroyer *Devastator*.

Atmosphere substation
Power substation
Hyperdrive
Deflector system

SHIPBOARD SYMBOLS

The components of functional systems within the Corvette are coded with symbols such as these for identification and maintenance purposes.

Main reactor
Ion accelerator
Customized fuel pre-cycler and turbo injectors
Ion pre-cycle impellers
Ion turbine
Thrust nozzle
Heat exhaust panel
Primary sensor array
Main corridor
Customized power feed manifold
C-3PO looks for R2-D2 in side corridor
Atmosphere tanks
Princess Leia gives R2-D2 the Death Star plans and her secret message for Obi-Wan Kenobi
Airlock doorway blasted through by TIE boarding craft
Magnetic safety shield generator ring contains atmosphere over hull breach at airlock
Pressurized fuel cell
Hyperdrive generator
Blast damage from the Star Destroyer Devastator overloaded the starboard shield projector, causing an explosion which damaged the power generator system. The main reactor had to be shut down, crippling the Tantive IV

THE CAPABLE CORVETTE

Sporting twin turbolaser turrets and a massive drive block of eleven ion turbine engines for speed, the Corellian Corvette balances defensive capabilities with a high power-to-mass ratio, meaning that what it can't shoot down it can generally outrun. The *Tantive IV* has been extensively refitted to suit Princess Leia's requirements, and the ship's original blue markings have been replaced with scarlet stripes to indicate the vessel's diplomatic status.

CONTRABANDITS

The Corvette's most notorious use is in the hands of Corellian smugglers. Blending anonymously into space traffic, these wily rogues pilot their vessels through Imperial security zones to avoid duties and taxes (or arrest for dealing in weapons and illegal goods). They are hard to spot, and chagrined Imperial officials have given the make its nickname "Blockade Runner."

ESCAPE POD

The small pod used by R2-D2 and C-3PO carries a minimum of equipment: simple rocket engines propel the pod away from danger as it ejects, using basic technology unaffected by magnetic or electrical interference. A gravity ring beneath the seat helps keep passengers secure above and cushions the shock of landing by projecting an antigravity field below. Only a single viewport is built in: a small slot window that is used for checking the landing environment before emerging. Fore and aft cameras feed a monitor inside to help it escape peril and find a suitable landing site.

Escape thrusters

Maneuvering jets

Viewscreen

Control panels

Gravity/ antigravity ring

Central floor plates retract after landing

Homing beacon and comlink set

Landing Systems Most pods are equipped with parachutes, repulsorlifts, and flotation devices to allow safe landings in a variety of environments.

NO-FRILLS DESIGN

Devoid of ornamentation or unnecessary features, the Corellian Corvette escape pod was designed so only the retro-rocket propulsion thrusters and attitude-control thrusters protrude from the cylindrical body, allowing the pod to neatly deploy from a starship's ejection tube. Instead of a single button or switch to open the hatch that leads directly to the open escape pod, the hatch is equipped with a cluster of pressure-sensitive tabs, designed for ease of use by various dexterous life forms. Although escape pods are generally off limits to droids, an astromech can extend a control arm to press the tabs.

Automatic Pilot Although most escape pods are equipped with a simple piloting station, the shipboard systems are heavily automated, enabling the pod to find and travel to the nearest habitable planet without a pilot at the controls.

IMPERIAL NAVY

After the Clone Wars, the Republic Navy of the Galactic Republic was reformed into the Imperial Navy, its purpose to enforce the Emperor's rule. Despite this transition, the Navy's mission remains largely the same: to eliminate hazards to profitable commerce in Imperial systems, assure the safety of member worlds from enemy forces, and to bolster planetary governments in times of crisis. The heart of the Imperial Navy are its enormous capital ships—the Star Destroyers.

Proton-shielded armor plate

Turret

Firing control

Blast cannon

Cooling system pumps

Power cells

Power feed and modulation control

Targeting level

Orbital Blockades Although it is impossible to garrison every inhabited world in Imperial space, the Navy can deploy its Star Destroyers to even remote planets in a short period of time. The very idea of an orbital blockade or bombardment encourages most worlds to comply with Imperial laws.

HEAVY BLASTER STATION

The heaviest weapons on board an *Imperial I*-class Star Destroyer are the six turbolaser turrets positioned with the two heavy ion cannon turrets along the flanks of the upper deck structure. Fifty meters in diameter, these turbolasers can overload deflector shields and punch holes in the most heavily armored spacecraft. While smaller, fast-moving ships are difficult to target with the turret guns, even a glancing hit from these cannons will destroy them.

Super Star Destroyers Impressive though *Imperial*-class Star Destroyers are, they are by no means the largest vessels in the fleet. Super Star Destroyers, such as Darth Vader's *Executor*, are many times larger and vastly more powerful, with crews numbering in the hundreds of thousands.

THE EVOLUTION OF THE STAR DESTROYER

The *Victory*-class Star Destroyer was developed in the final years of the Old Republic as a top-of-the-line peacekeeping battleship. Under the Emperor's rule, these have been superseded by the new *Imperial*-class Star Destroyers. At 1,600 meters in length these dwarf their predecessors. Darth Vader's Star Destroyer *Devastator*, with which he captures *Tantive IV*, is of the *Imperial I*-class type. *Imperial II*-class Star Destroyers make up the fleet which captures the rebel base on Hoth. Lord Vader leads this fleet from the *Executor*, first of the Super Star Destroyers, over eight times as large as the *Imperial*-class ships.

Main engine turbine

Backup engine reactor

Tractor beam targeting array

Command bridge

Heavy turbolaser battery

Starboard main engine thrust nozzle

Heavy ion cannon turret

Heavy turbolaser turret

Turret traverse motors

Turbolaser turret auxiliary power cells

Subsidiary reactor

Turbolaser station

Rebel prisoners

TIE boarding craft

Landing barge

Sentinel-class landing craft with Commander Praji's landing search team boarding

AT-AT

Flight deck control

Captured Tantive IV

Electromagnetic paralyzing pincer crane

Lateral quad laser battery

Anti-resonance plates

Primary power generator

TIE bombers are kept protected in armored compartments to limit damage if their bombs are set off

TIE bombers launch from the stern-most of the TIE launch hangars

HANGAR VIEW

This view from the main TIE landing bay shows the captured *Tantive IV* held by tractor beams and magnetic paralyzing pincer lock. Rebel prisoners are being escorted out of a TIE boarding craft for interrogation. In the background, the attack hangar can be seen with one set of armored doors open. Stormtrooper Commander Praji supervises the preparation of a landing search team that will scour the dunes of Tatooine below for the stolen plans to the Death Star.

STAR DESTROYER

The Star Destroyer is a symbol of the Empire's military might, carrying devastating firepower and assault forces anywhere in the galaxy to subjugate opposition. A Star Destroyer can easily overtake most fleeing craft, blasting them into submission or drawing them into its main hangar with tractor beams. *Imperial*-class Star Destroyers are 1,600 meters long, bristling with turbolasers and ion cannons, and equipped with eight giant turret gun stations. Star Destroyers carry 9,700 stormtroopers and a full wing of 72 TIE ships (typically including 48 TIE/In fighters, 12 TIE bombers, and 12 TIE boarding craft) as well as a range of attack and landing craft. A single Star Destroyer can overwhelm an entire rebellious planet. Major industrialized worlds are usually assaulted with a fleet of six Star Destroyers operating with support cruisers and supply craft. Such a force can obliterate any defenses, occupying or completely destroying cities or settlements.

The *Devastator*
An *Imperial I*-class Star Destroyer, the *Devastator* serves as Darth Vader's flagship when he pursues the *Tantive IV* to Tatooine, and is part of his fleet, Death Squadron. The *Devastator* also carries Vader's elite stormtrooper unit, the 501st Legion.

Axial defense turret

Flight deck control

Armored doors of attack hangar, where landing craft are launched and landed

Tantive IV, held in main hangar

Command Bridge Only high-ranking officers have the privilege to gaze through the large windows that line a Star Destroyer's bridge. The remaining crew perform their duties in sunken pits without any window views to distract them from their sensor scopes.

Main TIE landing bay

Auxiliary reactor

Tractor beam power cells

Pursuit tractor beams

TIE fighter service and fueling bays

Raw materials

TIE fighters and bombers land in the main TIE landing bay and are transferred to these TIE launch hangars in transfer carriers

Liquid stores

Shuttle craft for high-ranking officials are deployed through the small forward hangar, which also serves as back-up to the main hangar

SANDCRAWLER

A leftover titan from a forgotten mining era long ago, the Jawa sandcrawler patrols the desert wastelands of Tatooine in search of metal salvage and minerals. Serving as home to an entire clan of Jawas, the sandcrawler migrates across a wide territory over the course of a year, hunting for the wrecks that dot Tatooine's surface from spaceship crashes through centuries past. Jawas also round up stray droids, junked vehicles, and unwanted metal of any kind from settlements and moisture farmers. Pitted and scoured by numberless sandstorms, the sandcrawler serves the Jawas as transport, workshop, traveling store, and safe protection from the untold dangers of the desert.

JAWA REPAIRS

Jawas are experts at making use of available components to repair machinery and can put together a working droid from the most surprising variety of scrap parts. However, they are notorious for peddling shoddy workmanship that will last just long enough for the sandcrawler to disappear over the horizon.

Case-hardened smashers crush minerals or compact metal for storage

Conveyor at top of elevator

Ore crusher

Drill grinders

Laser pre-processor

Power generators

Reactor powers entire sandcrawler

Engineering station

Maintenance passage

Reactor melts processed ore and metal into a superheated cascade

Power cell

Ingots are extruded from purified underlevels of slag pool

Primary drive

Rear treads non-steerable, for drive only

Electrostatic repellers keep sand from interior components

Steam-heating array

Extensible starboard boarding gantry

Repulsorlift tube energizer

Extensible repulsorlift tube

Mobile Home For a clan of Jawas, the metal skin of the sandcrawler is all that stands between them and the terrors of Sand People and desert monsters.

DANGEROUS PRIZES

The furious winds of Tatooine's storm season can scour ancient spacewrecks from the deep sands of the Dune Sea. Jawa sandcrawlers venture into remote territories after the storms, searching for newly exposed prizes. Larger finds may cause them to call in other sandcrawlers to share in the processing. Field smelting factories and awnings are quickly erected as the Jawa work to beat the arrival of the next storm.

Transfer crane

Sleeping quarters

R1-G4 Reactor drone

Salvaged machinery being recycled

Magnet crane

Decoy pod from Tantive IV

Moisture vaporator

Control room

Navigation tracking room

Spotter's station

Cockpit

Sensors

Salvage crane

Intake to main conveyor belt, for ore and salvaged items

THE OLD MINING DAYS

The many sandcrawlers used by Jawa clans were built long ago during a mining boom on Tatooine, before the settlers arrived. The fleet of sandcrawlers ranged throughout the uncharted territories, encountering fearsome desert creatures and pursuing the valuable minerals found on the salt flats and dune fields. As the years passed, it was discovered that the most valuable minerals were found only on the surface. The mining era faded and Jawas later took over the abandoned sandcrawlers.

Auxiliary forward hatch

R2-D2

C-3PO

Jawa with droid caller

Heavy tread gearing does not become fouled by grit

Drive wheel

Conveyor

Steerable front treads

Main ramp hydraulic extenders

Primary ore hold converted into droid prison

Ramp opens to bring in wrecked vehicles, deploy mining or salvage machines, or to release droids for sale

Search and Rescue When a recently purchased R2 unit goes missing, Luke Skywalker enlists the help of the droid C-3PO, and heads out in his landspeeder to find the lost R2.

Duraplex windshield

Foot pedals control velocity

Communications receiver rotates in direction of best signal

Fuel filler cap

Control lever adjusts ride-height by varying power to the repulsor emitters

Wheel controls direction

Seat tractor units keep occupants safe

Primary terrain scanner

Hood attachment brackets

Fuel tank

Fuel tank baffles

Drop-down night vision headlights

Repulsor emitter cover

Fuel filler neck

Antigravity conduit

Multifunction navigation/ entertainment screens

Fuel lines

Repulsor vent grille

Electromagnetic small particle ejector has been removed for repair

Fuel management node

EXPOSED TURBINE

A few days prior to meeting the droids R2-D2 and C-3PO, the converter coil wires in the landspeeder's left turbine engine burned out, indicating a faulty regulator. Luke left the turbine's cowling off to prevent overheating.

Small particle ejector vent

Internal engine damage caused by missing particle ejector

Lower surface of landspeeder used for venting the considerable heat generated by all systems

Port eng mounts

Fan drive motor

Cooling fan

Radiator matrix

Coolant flow and return pipes

LUKE'S LANDSPEEDER

Intake shroud

Electromagnetic small particle filter prevents small debris from entering the engine

Primary fan

Multi-stage compressor

Large particle filter screen

Combustion chamber

Engine drive turbine

Bypass air outlet

Control links to engines

Thrust nozzle

Top engine mount

Starboard anti-gravity generator assembly

Fuel lines to top engine

Anti-gravity unit power input

Heat sink

Rear repulsor emitters integral with anti-gravity generator

Neutrino exhaust vent

Gaskets are essential in harsh desert climate on Tatooine

Power generator: All major systems are duplicated and have sufficient capacity to keep craft airborne in the event of component failure

Luke Skywalker's late-model SoroSuub X-34 landspeeder is one of his few sources of excitement. Having been raised by his Uncle Owen Lars and Aunt Beru on their Tatooine moisture farm, Luke obtained the landspeeder after Owen asked him to take responsibility for more moisture vaporators across their vast property. Luke argued that the most efficient way to inspect and maintain the vaporators would be to have his own landspeeder, and Owen grudgingly allowed Luke to purchase the poor-condition SoroSuub X-34 for 2,400 credits. The open cockpit seats a driver and a passenger, and built-in magnetic clamps behind the seats can secure droids or small cargo modules. The windshield is designed to close to a sealed bubble, but Luke keeps the cockpit open because he has yet to fix the shield's back half. Luke has put considerable time into restoring the vehicle, and uses the best parts he can afford to upgrade the repulsorlifts and turbine engines.

DESERT RACER

Luke knew little of his father, Anakin, but he inherited Anakin's restless nature, mechanical aptitude, and predilection for high-speed thrills. Luke and his friends spend many hours racing their landspeeders across Tatooine's desert flats and through the deep ravines beyond the Dune Sea. Luke has become adept at shooting womp rats with his laser rifle while driving the speeder at near-maximum speed.

VALUABLE PARTS

Because Tatooine has few factories or significant manufacturing facilities, the planet depends heavily on imported technology and recycled materials. Left unattended, a landspeeder makes a tempting target for Tusken Raiders, who by tradition transform scavenged metal into lethal weapons.

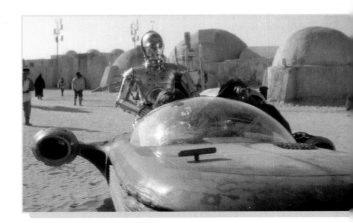

Mid-Air Parking Like most landspeeders, Luke's vehicle continues to hover above the ground after he has brought it to a complete stop.

MILLENNIUM FALCON

Battered, scarred, and much-modified, Han Solo's *Millennium Falcon* looks more like a bad scrap job than one of the fastest spaceships in the galaxy. This remarkable Corellian pirate ship began its life as a YT-1300 stock light freighter, but like many ships of its class the *Falcon* went through significant remodeling at the hands of smuggler captains. Its engines have doubled in size, its defenses are military-grade heavy-duty destructive weapons, and in every respect it is a high-performance hot rod of the highest caliber. The extensive modifications bring a price, however, in the form of endless maintenance. Solo makes his living by smuggling everything from weapons to contraband spices through Imperial blockades in the quest for profit outside the Empire's restrictive laws.

A LONG HISTORY

Han Solo won the *Millennium Falcon* from his old friend and fellow smuggler Lando Calrissian in a heated game of sabacc. Lando had no right to complain, having come to own the *Falcon* through gambling in the first place. Over many years, dozens of minor laser hits and micrometeoroid punctures have been patched with micro-panels (or even left alone), giving the ship a dilapidated appearance. Han Solo now refuses to clean up his ship's appearance as a matter of pride.

Hydraulic system

Boarding ramp

Secre compa ments

Concealed blaster cannon

Number two hold

Registry marking

Life support systems

Outboard power adapters

Maintenance access bay

De-Gausser

Mandible

Freight loading arm

Concussion missiles

Hyperspace integrator

Forward floodlight

Electromagnetic freight barge clamp

Passive sensor antenna

Freight loading doors

Landing jet

Freight loading room

Anti-concussion field generator

Warp vortex stabilizer

Deflector shield projector

Deflector shield generator

Main hold

Main sensor rectenna

Auxiliary inertial compensator

Lower quad laser turret

De-Gausser

Engineering station

Stolen laser power cell

Heat exhaust vent

Upper quad laser cannon

Power core

Rear freight elevator

Escape pod

CUSTOMIZATION

Two quad laser cannons, mounted above and below the ship's center, provide excellent protection for the *Falcon*. These extremely illegal military-grade blasters are just one of many augmented systems on board. The oversized top-of-the-line sensor dish on the port side can alert Captain Solo to Imperial ships before they become aware of his presence.

Fuel drive pressure stabilizer

Fuel driver

Hyperdrive

Sublight engines

Thrust vector plate

Thrust vector magnet

Sublight drive exhaust

Rear hover pad and landing gear

Crew's quarters

Circuitry bay

Hyperspace Journey
Outside the *Falcon*, hyperspace resembles a cascade of bright-blue bursts of energy. Every jump through hyperspace is carefully calculated by the ship's navicomputer to ensure the ship reaches her destination in one piece.

Port docking ring

Added armor plate

Blast damage

Sensor processing systems

Main fuel line

Fuel cooling system

Fuel tank stores Falcon's highly unstable dangerous liquid metal fuel

THE SECRETS OF SPEED

The *Falcon*'s customized hyperdrive system is fully twice the size of the drive system in a standard YT-1300 freighter, giving the ship a hyperdrive class of 0.5, twice as fast as Imperial warships. The secret of its hyperdrive performance is in Solo's modifications that "streamline" the ship in hyperspace, controlling the warp of the space-time continuum around it. Other ships have tried to match the *Falcon*'s speed without these modifications, and have blown themselves to subatomic particles.

"WHAT A PIECE OF JUNK!"

Like most people, Luke Skywalker has difficulty finding any obvious qualities in the *Millennium Falcon* when he first views the ship, but he soon discovers that the *Falcon*'s ramshackle appearance belies the fact that she is one of the fastest ships in the galaxy. Thanks to the *Falcon* crew's innovations with sensor-jamming technology, even the sophisticated scanners used by authorities in Imperial space and the Corporate Sector fail to detect the *Falcon*'s unique capabilities.

GALACTIC ADVENTURES

After capturing the *Millennium Falcon* near the remains of the planet Alderaan, Imperial boarding parties find nothing remarkable about the *Falcon*'s grimy interior, and their scanners fail to detect any lifeforms on board. Unknown to them, Captain Han Solo has concealed compartments for smuggling, and the below-deck chambers also prove useful for hiding crew and passengers. The ship's occupants escape, rescue the captive Princess Leia, and assist in the destruction of the first Death Star, striking a crucial blow against the Empire.

Docking Bay 94 Typical of the landing bays scattered throughout Mos Eisley Spaceport, Docking Bay 94 is simply a large, open-roof pit with reinforced walls.

Dejarik Gameboard At Chewbacca's urging, the *Falcon* was equipped with a Dejarik Hologame table. This table projects a range of holographic games on a surface of checkered circles. Dejarik chess is shown here.

M'onnok

Ng'ok

Grimtaash the Molator

Kintan Strider

Mantellian Savrip

K'lor'slug

Ghhhk

Houjix

Quick Getaway Docking Bay 94's old walls were designed to withstand the backblast of ion sublight engines. When attacked by Imperial stormtroopers, the *Falcon*'s repulsorlift engines allow for a hasty exit through the bay's open roof.

Blind Spot The *Millennium Falcon* escapes the pursuing Star Destroyer *Avenger* by hiding in a sensor blind spot on the rear of its bridge conning tower

Reunion on Cloud City
Han Solo lands the damaged *Falcon* in Cloud City, where he seeks help from Lando Calrissian, the *Falcon*'s previous owner.

The Battle of Endor
At the controls of the *Falcon*, Lando Calrissian leads the rebel fleet into battle against the second Death Star.

SHIP OF DESTINY

Years later, the *Millennium Falcon* is one of many ships forced to flee from the secret rebel base on Hoth, in the face of an Imperial assault. Han Solo guides the *Falcon* into the Hoth system's asteroid belt to escape the pursuing Imperial warships, despite the probability of successfully navigating an asteroid field being approximately 3,720:1. In need of repairs to the *Falcon*'s hyperdrive, Han then reluctantly travels to Cloud City in the Bespin system, and seeks help from the *Falcon*'s former owner, Lando Calrissian. However, in the process he is captured by the infamous bounty hunter Boba Fett. Once again under the command of Lando Calrissian, the *Falcon* subsequently plays a pivotal role in the climactic Battle of Endor, leading the assault on the second Death Star, and successfully destroying the giant battle station.

Tight Squeeze Lando pilots the *Falcon* through the second Death Star's skeletal superstructure to destroy the battle station's reactor core. The *Falcon* proves more nimble on sharp turns than the pursuing Imperial TIE fighters.

DETENTION BLOCK AA-23

A desperate plan takes Luke, Han, and Chewbacca into the heart of peril as they try to rescue Princess Leia. Disguised as stormtroopers, Luke and Han escort Chewbacca, their "prisoner," into Leia's detention block. The supervisor suspects trouble, and only immediate action will save the rebels.

TRASH COMPACTOR 32-6-3827

Escaping Leia's cell block, the rebels dive into a garbage chute and land in a trash compactor, where refuse of every kind is collected before being processed and dumped into space.

AIR SHAFT

Throughout the Death Star are vast air shafts. Extendable bridges connect passages across the shafts, but can be disabled. When Luke and Leia find themselves trapped at one of the air shafts, quick thinking and bravery provide the only way across.

TRACTOR BEAM REACTOR COUPLING

The Death Star tractor beam is coupled to the main reactor in seven locations. These power terminals stand atop generator towers 35 kilometers tall. The air is taut with high-voltage electricity throughout the shaft surrounding the tower. It is in this setting that Ben Kenobi secretly deactivates one of the power beams to allow the *Millennium Falcon* to escape.

CHALLENGE AND SACRIFICE

Darth Vader senses the presence of his old Jedi master Obi-Wan Kenobi aboard the Death Star, and confronts him alone in a deadly lightsaber duel. Kenobi sacrifices himself to help his young friends escape, yielding to Vader in an empty victory in which, mysteriously, Obi-Wan becomes one with the Force.

Tractor beam power coupling deactivated by Ben Kenobi

Secondary power converters

Power processing networks

Atmosphere processing unit

Ion drive reactor

Atmosphere processing substation

Equatorial docking bay

Ion sublight engines

DEATH STAR

The Empire's gigantic battle station code-named Death Star is 160 kilometers in diameter, large enough to be mistaken for a small moon. Credited as the brainchild of Grand Moff Tarkin, this colossal superweapon is designed to enforce the Emperor's rule through terror, presenting both the symbol and reality of ultimate destructive power. Making use of the Empire's most advanced discoveries in super-engineering, the Death Star is built around a hypermatter reactor that can generate enough power to destroy an entire planet. Designed in secret on the planet Geonosis and built by slave labor and titanic factory machines, the Death Star's vast structure houses over a million individuals and thousands of armed spacecraft, making it capable of occupying whole star systems by force. Elite gunners and troopers man the station's advanced weapons. The Death Star, once fully operational, represents a chilling specter of totalitarian domination and threatens to extinguish all hope for freedom in the galaxy.

Main exhaust port

Thermal exhaust port shaft runs through central power column

Equatorial trench

Inner decks stacked

Surface decks concentric

THE STOLEN PLANS

A complete technical readout of the battle station (left) was stolen by rebel spies. These plans reveal the overwhelming might of the Death Star, detailing its myriad weapons systems and immense power structures. Ion engines, hyperdrives, and hangar bays ring the station's equatorial trench, while power cells over 15 kilometers wide distribute energy throughout the thousands of internal decks of the station. Air shafts and void spaces honeycomb the interior. Occupying the polar axis of the Death Star is its central power column, with the hypermatter reactor at its core. However, the Death Star's powerful defenses have one fatal flaw—small thermal exhaust ports that lead from the surface to the heart of the main reactor.

ALDERAAN DESTROYED

Without hesitation Grand Moff Tarkin orders the destruction of the peaceful planet Alderaan as the first demonstration of the Death Star's power. As the superlaser lances out at the blue-green planet, this horrific act wipes out billions of people.

SUPERLASER TRIBUTARY BEAM SHAFT

Eight tributary beams unite to form the superlaser primary beam. These tributary beams are arranged around the invisible central focusing field, firing in alternate sequence to build the power necessary to destroy a planet. The titanic energy of these beams must be monitored to prevent imbalance explosions.

TIE FIGHTER

TIE fighters are the most visible image of the Empire's wide-reaching power, and the TIE engine is the most precisely manufactured propulsion system in the galaxy. Solar arrays collect light energy, channeling it through a reactor to fire emissions from a high-pressure radioactive gas. The engine has no moving parts, reducing its maintenance requirements. These lightweight ships are built without defensive shields, hyperdrives or life support systems, so the pilots must wear spacesuits. TIE fighters gain speed and maneuverability at the price of fragility, and reliance on nearby Imperial bases or vessels for support.

ALL THE SAME

TIE pilots may never use the same ship twice, and develop no sentimental attachment to their craft as rebels often do. TIE pilots know that every reconditioned fighter is identical to a factory-fresh ship; one is the same as many thousands—another reinforcement of Imperial philosophy of absolute conformity.

Solar energy collectors

Solar array support frame

Heat exchange matrix

Energy accumulator lines

Cockpit access hatch

Main viewport

Pilot in spacesuit

Power lines

Phase two energy collection coils

Power line

Fuel line

Low temperature laser tip

High-pressure radioactive gas fuel tank

Fuel tank cap

Energy grid monitor

TIE MISSION PROFILES

TIE fighters are deployed for a variety of mission profiles. Their primary role is as space superiority fighters, engaging rebel craft and defending Imperial bases and capital ships. Scout TIEs may travel alone to cover wide areas of space. Such individual scouts patrol the huge asteroid field left by the explosion of the planet Alderaan. Ships are assigned to escort duty in pairs, such as the twin TIEs that escort all flights of the Emperor's shuttle. Regular sentry groups of four TIE fighters patrol the space around Imperial bases, stations, and capital starships. A typical TIE fighter attack squadron consists of 12 ships, and a full attack wing consists of six squadrons, or 72 TIE fighters.

Upgraded Lasers
Originally, TIE laser cannons drew power from the ion engines. Because this reduced maneuverability in heavy combat when the lasers were used frequently, a separate power generator has been installed to increase the lasers' range and lethality.

Retaining claw

TIE in launch position

Pilots' boarding gantry

Transfer tunnel

Pilot boarding ship

Hangar control room

Elevator well

Service gantry

TIE arriving from landing hangar

Service droid

TIE HANGAR

TIEs are launched from cycling racks of up to 72 ships. Pilots board the TIEs from overhead gantries and the ships are released into space as they disengage from the front position in the rack system. Returning ships land in separate hangars, where they are guided into receiver-carriers by small tractor beams. The receivers carry the TIE to a debarkation station where the pilot exits. From there the TIE may be serviced and refueled in a separate bay on its way through transfer tunnels to a launch hangar. In the launch hangar the TIE is cycled into the launch rack, ready for its next mission.

PILOT PSYCHOLOGY

TIE fighters lack landing gear, a measure designed to reduce mass for maximum maneuverability. While the ships are structurally capable of sitting on their wings, they are not designed to land or disembark pilots without special support. This teaches the pilots to rely completely on higher authority.

Overbridge

Beam emitter
crystal

Primary beam
focusing magnet

Targeting field
generator

Static discharge
tower

Star Destroyer

Docking Bay 327

Magnetic
shielding

Hyperdrive

Tributary superlaser
beam shaft

Induction hyperphase
generator

Firing field
amplifier

Main power
generator

Carrier beam
crystal

Primary power
amplifier

Insulator plating

Hypermatter reactor

DOCKING BAY 327

Drawn in by a tractor beam, the *Millennium Falcon* comes to rest in a pressurized hangar within the Death Star's equatorial trench. Magnetic shields over the entrance retain the atmosphere. Outboard power-feeds hook up to landed craft so that the ship reactors can be shut down while in the hangar.

ASSAULT ON THE POLAR TRENCH

The exhaust port target of the rebel assault is protected in a trench, which is in turn protected by a hail of fire from deadly turbolaser towers on the Death Star surface. To bomb the exhaust port, the rebel fighters must maneuver down the trench beneath the fire zone, but they find themselves pursued closely by Imperial TIE fighters and Darth Vader himself. The defense is lethal: all but three of the rebel fighters are destroyed.

OVERBRIDGE

The primary control room of the Death Star is the overbridge, situated at the top edge of the superlaser dish. From this nerve center Grand Moff Tarkin commands the gigantic battle station. The staff feeds critical information to the main viewscreen.

EXHAUST PORT

The rebels target this two-meter-wide thermal exhaust port as their one chance of destroying the Death Star. Red Leader's shot at the small port is only a near miss.

Target exhaust shaft

Concentric surface structure

Power cell

Tractor beam
generator tower

T-65 X-WING

The X-wing starfighter was a top-secret project of the Incom Corporation when the Empire began to suspect rebel sympathies within the company and seized its assets. Key members of the design team escaped with the plans and two prototypes, destroying all other records of the ship. Hence, into the hands of the Rebellion came what would become its finest space fighter. Carrying heavy firepower, hyperdrive, and defensive shields, the X-wing is nonetheless maneuverable enough for close combat with the Empire's lethally agile TIE fighters. Although a formidable space superiority fighter, the X-wing's complex systems and rare alloys have delayed full-scale production of the craft for years.

INSIDE THE COCKPIT
The X-wing's highly responsive maneuverability can make it a dangerous craft for new pilots to handle. In addition to the fairly straightforward flight control systems, comprehensive cockpit displays allow the pilot to monitor and control energy distribution throughout the ship's systems during combat.

The on-board R2 astromech droid carries out hyperspace calculations and handles in-flight operational adjustments and damage control

Cockpit canopy

Pitch and roll control pedals

Laser firing tip

Sensor computer

Communications antenna

Sensor window

Primary sensor array

Nose cone

Enemy sensor jammer unit

Forward landing gear

Hydraulic lines

Repulsorlift

Flight computer

Proton torpedo

Farmboy to Fighter Pilot
Luke Skywalker had never piloted an Incom Corporation X-wing prior to the Battle of Yavin. However, his experience flying an Incom T-16 Skyhopper through the twisting canyons on Tatooine proves invaluable when he enters the Death Star's polar trench.

INDEPENDENT OPERATION
Hyperdrive and the ability to launch and land without special support enable the X-wing to operate independently, unlike Imperial TIE fighters. The X-wing is equipped with life support sufficient for one week in space: air, water, food, and life-process support equipment are packed into the area behind the pilot's seat. When the ship lands, the air supply can be renewed, and the water and life support systems partially recharged. A cargo bay carries survival gear for pilots who land in hostile environments.

Electromagnetic gyros

Retro-thrust nozzle

Life support

THE DOG-FIGHTING EDGE

The X-wing achieves its remarkable maneuverability through a combination of three factors. Differential thrust from its four fusial ion engines is the first. High-mass electromagnetic gyros in each of the four retro thrusters add a turning effect that helps to swing the ship in tight curves. Finally, precise bursts of retro-thrust fire forward through the turbine nozzles to add further control and give the ship a crucial edge in combat.

Reactant injector

Turbo impeller

Exhaust nozzle

Deflector shield generator

Hyperdrive

Deflector shield projectors

Upper laser cannon mount

Cargo bay

Targeting computer screen (switched off)

Inertial compensator

Power converters rephase energy for ship subsystems

Power generator

Power coupling

Fusial ion thrust engine

Laser generator

Laser cooling sleeve

LASER CANNONS

The X-wing's laser generators operate at the limits of safety to generate maximum destructive power. The long cannons of the X-wing develop longer range for its lasers, which can engage an oncoming enemy before the enemy can return fire.

Laser cannon

Magnetic flashback suppressors keep the occasional unstable laserbolt from damaging the cannon

After Luke Skywalker and the crew of the *Millennium Falcon* rescue Princess Leia from the Death Star, they flee across space with an unwelcome passenger: an Imperial homing beacon. This allows Imperial forces to trace the *Falcon* to her destination, the rebels' secret base on the moon Yavin 4. As the ponderous Death Star crawls across hyperspace to the Yavin system, the rebels discover a crucial flaw in the battle station's design, and race to form a plan of attack before Grand Moff Tarkin makes Yavin 4 his next target for annihilation.

Improvised Hangar The ancient Great Temple on Yavin 4 serves as the headquarters for the Rebel Alliance. Rebel engineers transformed the temple's ground floor and underground levels into hangars for starfighters and transports.

Proton warhead

A high-energy launch cartridge fires each torpedo, giving it thrust and trajectory guidance through a precise gyroscopic spin

Arming power shell

Guidance gyro

Rebel Squadrons Skirting the orbit of the gas giant Yavin, X-wing and Y-wing starfighters fly toward the Death Star. The groups include Red Squadron, which consists of X-wings, and Gold Squadron with Y-wings.

DESTROYER OF THE DEATH STAR

Proton torpedoes such as the MG7-As carried by the X-wing and Y-wing are extremely dangerous focused nuclear explosives. They are used for critical target destruction or to punch through ray shielding that will deflect laser weapons. Proton torpedoes are very expensive and available to Alliance forces only in limited numbers. Luke Skywalker carries only a single pair for his critical shots that destroy the Death Star.

Attack Formation Innovative twin-split "S-foil" wings give the X-wing improved performance in atmospheric flight. In combat, the wings deploy in an "X" shape, increasing weapons coverage.

Y-WING: REBEL WORKHORSE

Originally produced by Koensayr Manufacturing for the Republic fleet during the Clone Wars, the BTL Y-wing is a combination starfighter and light bomber, and is the most prevalent fighter in the Rebel Alliance. Koensayr produced several different models, adapted for different missions, including one-man and two-man versions, but most of the Alliance's Y-wings are so stripped down that they only skeletally resemble the stock models. The Y-wing's solid construction weathers combat damage that would destroy similar-sized fighters, and has earned its reputation as the workhorse of the rebel fighting forces.

Tunnel Vision The Y-wing's cockpit offers limited visibility when compared with later Alliance fighter designs such as the T-65 X-wing or RZ-1 A-wing.

ORIGINAL SPLENDOR

Originally all versions of the the Y-wing were entirely sheathed in body shells (right), including the BTL-B heavy bomber variant, which was notable for its bulkier hull design. Because the aged ships in the rebel fleet require constant repairs, aggravated rebel technicians, tired of removing body hull panels to access inner machinery, opted to remove the panels permanently. The Alliance's Y-wings have been so heavily repaired and modified that no two of them are identical.

Heat radiator vents

Heat vents

Because Y-wing's laser systems are low-maintenance, nose cones have been kept intact

Maintenance access

Engines before custom turbo modifications

This Y-wing is a BTL-A4, which seats a single pilot. Other versions include the Longprobe BTL-A4, equipped with extra provisions and enhanced sensors, and the BTL-S3, a two-seater in which a gunnery officer replaces the augmented targeting computer equipment featured in the BTL-A4

Fiery End Ambushed from behind, the Y-wings of Gold Squadron are wiped out one after another.

Trench Tactics Speeding through the Death Star trench to reach their target, the pilots of Gold Squadron switch all power to their Y-wings' front deflector screens to defend themselves against a barrage of enemy fire.

BTL-A4 Y-WING

B uilt to last and made to last even longer by dedicated
Rebel Alliance mechanics, most of the Y-wings in the
rebel fleet are over two decades old. The Y-wings have
been retrofitted for Taim & Bak laser cannons, ArMek light
ion cannons, and Arakyd flex tube proton torpedo launchers.
Like most rebel starfighters, the Y-wing is equipped with a
hyperdrive but requires an astromech unit to fully calculate
the necessary course vectors and power settings for any
hyperspace jump. Although it is not as fast, maneuverable,
or heavily armed as other starfighters, the Y-wing remains
a potent craft for its ability to endure and deliver
tremendous punishment.

Hyperdrive sequencer

Hyperdrive tachyon exhaust

Deflector shield projectors

Deflector shield
generator

Hyperdrive
arc housing

Main power cell

Engine housing

Vectral ring

Thrust vectrals

Heavy ion jet turbines,
built to last

Exhaust nozzle

Wing
repulsorlift

Ion fission reactor

Custom ion
turbo injector

Pulse electromagnets
accelerate ionized fuel for
injection into turbines

Long-range
targeting
sensor array

ION CANNONS

Ion cannons fire an electrical charge to disrupt the control circuits of an enemy craft
without destroying it. The Y-wing features twin ion cannons, but they are notoriously
delicate instruments. Their crystal matrices invariably get vibrated out of alignment in
flight and combat, and rebel mechanics hate them for the time they cost in maintenance.
For the attack on the Death Star, only two Y-wings in the entire rebel force had functioning
ion cannons. These proved critically useful, and one of these craft was the only Y-wing to
survive the battle.

COOLING SYSTEM

The Y-wing runs very hot for a ship of its size, and employs a complicated
cooling system that runs throughout the ship. Parts of this system need
maintenance after every flight. Coolant tubes are often jerry-rigged by rebel
mechanics when leaks render inaccessible sections frustratingly inoperative.

Ion jet engine

Composite sensor dome protects delicate instruments

Targeting computer

Twin ion cannons

Ion cannon charge generators

Astromech droid

Coolant pipe

Main coolant pump

Twin power generators are compact and durable

Life support equipment

Neck repulsorlift

Inertial compensator

Laser generator heat sink

Coolant coils

Torpedo loader

Proton torpedo launch racks

Proton torpedo

Main laser coolant pump

Cockpit

Boarding ladder

Heavy-duty long-range laser cannons extend through length of ship's nose cone

Harmonic vibration damper

Harmonic field sensor

Laser tip

Nose cone

Forward laser coolant pump

Forward landing gear

Torpedo launch tube

TWIN SENSOR SYSTEMS

The Y-wing's secondary role as a bomber craft requires a tandem long-range sensor set to provide binocular range-finding. When both sets are working, the Y-wing offers slightly better targeting precision than the X-wing—one reason why Y-wings were the primary attack craft in the Death Star trench.

Rebel Retrofit Prior to the attack on the Death Star, Rebel Alliance technicians make sure all late-model Y-wings are equipped with two Arakyd proton torpedo launchers, each of which holds four MG7-A torpedoes.

Targeting Computer Like the X-wing, the Y-wing utilizes the IN-344-B "Sightline" holographic imaging system.

TIE ADVANCED X1

When rebel spacecraft attacked the original Death Star, Darth Vader himself took a fighter into combat against them. He piloted a TIE Advanced x1 prototype, the latest fighter development from the Empire's Sienar Fleet Systems. It is a more capable ship than the standard TIE/In fighters, with a more sophisticated target tracking system and an augmented engine assembly fed by high-conversion solar cells on its bent wings, giving deadly speed and maneuverability. Unlike standard TIEs, it has both protective shields and hyperdrive capability. The hyperdrive saved Vader after the Death Star was destroyed, enabling him to reach an Imperial outpost and return to power.

High-performance solar cells

Power carrier pulse generator

Auxiliary fuel capsule

Exhaust nozzle

Deflector shield generator

Hyperdrive capacitor

Hyperdrive thermal radiator ports

Hyperdrive power module

Hyperdrive

Energizer

Power cell

Secondary power distributor

Rear deflector shield projector

Stabilizing field projector bar

Solar power collector line

EXPERIMENTAL SHIELDS

While the standard TIE fighter carries no shields, the x1 is strengthened and protected by an experimental deflector shield system. A stabilizing field is projected by a supermagnet at the rear of the ship, while deflector energies are deployed from forward and lateral pairs of projector bars. These experimental deflector bars sometimes require last-minute tuning for best performance, and x1s have gone into combat more than once with the deflector bar maintenance access panels removed.

Solar power phase one converter

Main support strut

Solar ionization reactor

Upper viewports

Access hatch

Frequency jammer

High-voltage power modulation package

SUPERIOR TARGETING

Imperial fighter craft carry advanced targeting equipment that gives them an advantage over the older modules used by rebel ships. The x1 employs a sophisticated target tracking system that offers even more accurate target acquisition than standard TIE fighters. This tracking system must overcome the powerful jamming signals used by all combat craft to defeat true electronic "target lock." For best combat performance, the system requires frequent re-adjustment by the pilot.

Targeting computer

Flight computer

Binocular sensor array

Forward deflector shield generator

Overdrive ion flux cooling system

Solar power phase two converter coils

Fuel line

Fuel recharge connection

Fuel tank holds radioactive gas under extremely high pressure

Low-temperature laser cannon

Laser tip

Laser power converter

Forward viewport

Laser mount

Dark Side Ace As a Jedi Knight, Darth Vader gained experience behind the controls of Jedi starfighters that lacked defensive energy shields. Consequently, although his TIE Advanced x1 is shield-equipped, Vader diverts all energy to engines and weapons.

ASSAULT CARRIERS

AT-AT walkers can unleash their assault forces in several rapid waves using drop-lines with attached harnesses. Boom racks extend to drop combat troops and equipment over the side. Speeder bikes are deployed using harnesses at the front and back.

Forward sensors

Class II heavy laser cannon

Medium blaster cannon

Viewport

Targeting computers

Blaster targeting rangefinder

Cockpit access tube

Laser power cell

Atmosphere intake

Up to 40 snowtroopers awaiting deployment

Backpack charger troop bench

High-speed cable winch

Upper deck officer

Extensible deployment cable rack

Energizer rods

Fuel cell

Deployment harness

Fuel pump

Deployment staging platform

Shock absorber

Piston drive pressurizer

Flat plate piston drive

Knee joint

Heavy braces at these points lock AT-ATs into their landing barges

Speeder bike garage

Knee joint

Imperial Assault After discovering a Rebel Alliance base on the ice planet Hoth, Imperial forces deploy AT-ATs to penetrate and destroy it.

ALL-TERRAIN ABILITIES

The thick armor plating of the Imperial walker makes it too heavy for effective repulsorlifts, hence its huge legs for striding over obstacles and rugged terrain. While steep hillsides or deep swamps can thwart the progress of the walker, AT-AT pilots can guide walkers across surprisingly rugged ground.

Battle of Hoth Although rebels manage to down a few AT-ATs, they are soon overwhelmed by the lumbering vehicles' heavy firepower.

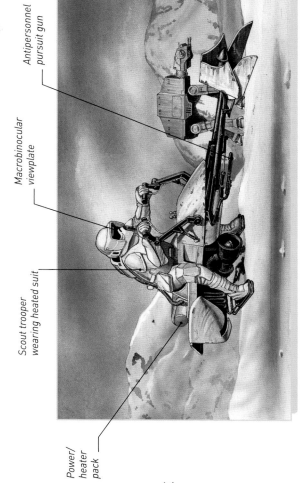

Antipersonnel pursuit gun

Macrobinocular viewplate

Scout trooper wearing heated suit

Power/ heater pack

SPEEDER BIKES

AT-AT walkers usually carry a set of high-velocity repulsorlift speeder bikes for scouting or survivor-hunting missions. The speed and agility of these bikes complement the plodding might of the walkers, making the combined assault capability thorough and overwhelming. The colossal size and nightmarish animal resemblance of the AT-AT combine with its combat strengths to give it tremendous psychological power. Until the Battle of Hoth, no army had ever fought resolutely against an onslaught of walkers, so frightening and devastating is their presence.

Ankle pitch brake

control systems

Footpad yaw strut

heavy armor

Service access cover

Footpad

Toe flap

Terrain sensor computer

Impulse terrain sensor

Terrain scanners

Toe flap piston

AT-AT

Deployed as weapons of terror, the gigantic Imperial All Terrain Armored Transport (AT-AT) walkers advance inexorably on the battlefield like unstoppable giants. These behemoth monsters are shielded with heavy armor cladding, making them invulnerable to all but the heaviest turbolaser weaponry. Blaster bolts from ordinary turrets and cannons merely glance off the walker's armor or are harmlessly absorbed and dissipated. A powerful reactor produces the raw energy needed to move this weighty battle machine. Cannons in the movable cockpit spit death at helpless foes below, cutting a swath of destruction which the mighty footpads then crash through. Breaking enemy lines with its blaster fire and lumbering mass, the walker also functions as a troop carrier, holding in its body platoons of crack assault soldiers, ground weaponry, and speeder bike antipersonnel/reconnaissance vehicles. When this cargo of terror is released into the chaos and destruction a walker has created, another Imperial victory is nearly complete.

AT-AT COCKPIT

The AT-AT's heavily armored head serves as a cockpit for the two pilots and the vehicle commander. On its exterior are mounted the vehicle's weapons systems. While both pilots are fully qualified to perform all control functions, in normal practice one serves as driver while the other acts as gunner. Firing controls can at any time be yielded to the vehicle commander, who uses a periscope display capable of tactical and photographic readouts. The two pilots are guided by terrain sensors under the cockpit and ground sensors built into the feet of the vehicle. Scans read the nature and shape of the terrain ahead, ensuring infallible footing.

Ringed electromagnet systems enable the neck to flex

Vehicle commander

Holographic communicator

Pilot

ASSAULT ARMOR DIVISION
Handpicked by Darth Vader to lead the Imperial Army's Assault Armor Division against the rebel forces on Hoth, General Maximilian Veers commands both the Thundering Herd AT-AT squadron and the elite Imperial snowtrooper unit Blizzard Force.

Elevated Advantage AT-ATs are highly conspicuous on open terrain, however AT-AT armor is nearly impervious to blaster fire, and the crew in the elevated command cockpit have a clear view of obstacles and targets over vast distances.

Periscope Display The AT-AT commander uses a periscope display mounted into the cockpit's ceiling, which provides enhanced views of targets, sensor readouts, and tactical data.

Heavy Cannons The AT-AT's two Taim & Bak MS-1 heavy laser cannons can be fired alternately in quick succession, or simultaneously for a single, powerful blast.

AT-ST

The scout walker, or All Terrain Scout Transport (AT-ST) walks easily through rugged terrain to carry out its missions. Reconnaissance, battle line support, and anti-personnel hunting make excellent use of the craft's armaments and capabilities. Faster than a full-size AT-AT, the scout walker is also able to step through denser terrain with greater ease, traveling through small canyons or forest that would stop an AT-AT. While AT-ATs crush main rebel defensive emplacements, AT-STs ferret out small pockets of resistance. Since the scout walker is almost impossible to flee on foot, the sight of patrolling AT-STs strikes fear into isolated ground troops.

The Cockpit View Viewscreens and holo-projectors allow AT-ST crew to see ahead and behind simultaneously. While the computer can guide the scout walker over even ground, an expert human pilot must balance the wide variety of data input and control the craft's walking in difficult terrain.

Scout Transport With a top speed of 90 kph (55.6 mph), the All Terrain Scout Transport (AT-ST) is faster and more maneuverable than an AT-AT, but less heavily armed and armored.

Locomotion computer

Weapons power converters

Cockpit cooling system

Entry hatch

Armor plate

Concussion charger

Handrail

Forward sensor

Command viewport

Light blaster cannon

Pilot

Face armor

Twin blaster cannons

Concussion launcher

Radiator

Exhaust

Drive engine

Gyro system

Gyro power cell

Plastron shield

Power cells

Joint shield

Knee joint

Sophisticated shock-absorbing systems within the legs of the scout walker keep it stable and feed balance data into the navigation computers

Elbow joint

Too small to carry an onboard full-power generator, the AT-ST uses disposable high-intensity power cells to feed its power-intensive systems. These power cells limit the range of the AT-ST

Sensors in the footpads of the scout walker offer detailed feedback on the terrain ahead, reading density and contour for precise foot placement

Fence-cutting blade

Cutter actuator

Shin

Ankle joint tensioner

Shin stabilizer/compression gearing assembly

Ankle joint

Footpad

Foot joint

Ground impact sensor

GYRO STABILIZED

With an expert pilot at the helm, an AT-ST can move with remarkable agility across a wide variety of terrain. A powerful gyro stabilizer coupled with a complex locomotion system allows the scout walker to mimic the walking movements of a living creature.

SNOWSPEEDER

Soon after establishing their new secret base on the ice planet Hoth, the rebels acquired a small squadron of Incom T-47 airspeeders to serve as defensive units. These airspeeders had been equipped with power converters and military-grade laser cannons. Highly maneuverable and fast, these airspeeders seemed ideal for the defense of Echo Base. The intense cold of Hoth initially proved too severe for the T-47s, until rebel technicians modified them to suit their new environment.

"Use your harpoons and tow cables. Go for the legs."
Luke Skywalker

Polarized view screen

Pilot

Gunner

Targeting sensors

Collimating tip

FROM CIVILIAN TO MILITARY USE

To convert the T-47 civilian airspeeder into a military craft, laser cannon assemblies were bolted to the wings. External power converters and a laser generator system tapped the extra energy of the T-47's powerful generators, and added armor plate strengthened the craft's hull. The result is a short-range attack craft of exceptionally high maneuverability. The rebel snowspeeder's civilian origins and small size explain its lack of defensive shields. In battle, the craft relies on its speed and agility to evade laser blasts.

Homing sensors

Armor plate

Laser barrel

Speeding to Battle Incom T-47 airspeeders are designed to fly in middle and upper atmospheres, but skilled pilots have little difficulty skimming planetary surfaces at high speed. The T-47's aerodynamic design allows turning without reducing speed, making it nearly impossible to track with flight-predictor sensors.

Final stage energizer

Laser generator

Power coupling

Laser activator

Armored canopy

Repulsor generator

Power generator

Cooling fins

Air brakes

Aft repulsor
unit housing

Insulator

ADAPTING TO THE COLD

The power generators of the T-47 run hot, requiring a large bank of heat radiator fins at the back of the craft for essential cooling. The rebels learned quickly that these were far too effective in the icy cold of Hoth, which caused the generators to lock up. Efforts to bypass the radiator system proved ineffective. In the end, rebel mechanics insulated each of the radiator fins with side panels to dampen their heat-exchange effect and keep the engine systems warm enough for optimal functioning. These adaptations were completed on some of the ships only minutes before the Imperial attack on Echo Base began.

ID markings

Harpoon and
tow cable

Repulsor
generator

Airbraking flap

Power
converter

Fuel tank

Flight Controls The T-47's flight control scopes jut upward slightly across the base of the front view screen, enabling the pilot to rely on peripheral vision to quickly glean data from the scopes.

Attacking the Walker Luke Skywalker devised the unorthodox strategy of attacking Imperial walkers with the snowspeeder's tow cable, designed for retrieving and hauling cargo sleds. Entangling the legs of the walker immobilized and tripped the giant assault vehicle, a victory for determination and bravery over raw strength.

Circuitry access

Air intake

Wingtip repulsor
projectors

TIE BOMBER

Derived from the TIE/gt variant of the TIE starfighter family, the TIE bomber was developed to take over the task of orbital bombardment from the Empire's capital ships. With its massive ordnance capacity, this formidable assault ship can be deployed against ground- and space-based targets, delivering its lethal load with pinpoint accuracy. The craft's precision targeting is an important capability—where capital ship bombardment often results in extensive collateral damage, the TIE bomber's ability to make "surgical strikes" enables specific targets to be taken out, while leaving surrounding facilities intact.

Ultra-high efficiency girondium-colium solar cells

Structural ties reinforce strength of angled solar-panel wing

Starboard command module

Flight controls

Transparisteel viewport

Energy grid monitoring computer

Solar power phase two converter coils

Heavy-duty power trunking carrying power from solar arrays

Pilot wears life-support body suit as an emergency back-up during space operations

Laser cannon (one of two mounted on either side of cockpit)

Cockpit emergency air supply (also used with high-altitude ejections)

Emergency survival kit

Precision Targeting Traveling over a large asteroid, two TIE bombers drop proton bombs into craters in an effort to flush out an elusive rebel ship.

THE TIE COMPANY

The TIE family of Imperial warcraft is probably the most recognizable product of Sienar Fleet Systems, one of the Empire's major military starship manufacturers. Founded by the powerful Sienar family, Republic Sienar Systems was one of the most successful starship manufacturers of the Old Republic. During the Republic's final days, the company was under the almost-exclusive control of the Senate. With the rise of the Empire, control was returned to Raith Sienar—a friend and cohort of Wilhuff Tarkin—by the direct order of the Emperor. Under the new name of Sienar Fleet Systems (SFS), the company's Imperial connections helped it secure lucrative military contracts. Sienar's loyalty to the Empire enabled his company to remain relatively independent when many other manufacturers were forcibly amalgamated or taken over. SFS is known by the nickname of "The TIE Company," but it also manufactures the *Lambda*-class shuttle, the *Interdictor* Cruiser, and the Skipray Blastboat.

PILOT SURVIVAL

Unlike most Imperial warcraft, the TIE bomber is equipped with a cockpit ejector seat. Pilots also have the luxury of a life support system in the cockpit, although they still wear flight suits in case of emergency.

SITTING DUCK

As the only "twin pod" in the TIE series, the TIE bomber is more robustly engineered than its fighter and interceptor stablemates. The vehicle is equipped with structural reinforcement to survive the back-blast from the bombardments it delivers—especially in planetary operations. Due to its greater power requirements, the bomber's solar panels are elongated, providing a greater energy-collecting surface area than the standard TIE starfighter. However, the bomber's bulky structure means it is also slower and far less maneuverable than other TIE craft, earning it the nickname "sitting duck" among rebel pilots, who consider it to be easy prey.

Electromagnetic pulse generator (used to disable enemy defense systems)

Cockpit air-scrubber

Pilot ingress/ egress hatch

Ejector seat

Retro-fire thruster

Missile-firing port force-field projector

Ordnance maneuvering arm loads armaments

Guided concussion missiles (proton torpedoes can also be carried)

Racked orbital mines

Waste-heat radiator panel

Reinforced wing pylons support large solar arrays

Inspection hatches

Energy collection hub

Combat-sensor array

Flight-control computer system

Maneuvering thruster

Module connection block housing SFS I-a2b solar ionization reactor for engines

Plasma transfer duct to starboard engine

Targeting sensors

Repulsorlift generator

Bomb-drop chute

Proton bomb

Ordnance pod can be converted to carry troops

Solar power phase one converter

BLAST POWER

Proton bombs form an important part of a TIE bomber's ordnance. These energy explosives produce a destructive cloud of high-velocity subatomic particles. They are especially effective against ray- and energy-shielded targets, but can be blocked by particle-deflector defenses.

PROTON BOMB

Implosion detonator

Neuranium reaction-containment shield

Lanthanide alloy outer skin

Implosion dampers

Proton-generating reactor core

TIE INTERCEPTOR

Fortunately for the rebels, Darth Vader's TIE Advanced x1 prototype proved too expensive for full-scale production. However, its high-performance solar cells and bent-wing configuration have survived in the form of the TIE interceptor—the most advanced mass-produced starfighter in the Imperial arsenal. Equipped with upgraded ion engines and four blaster cannons, the TIE interceptor is faster, more maneuverable, and better armed than any of its predecessors, and outperforms all other craft in a dogfight. To achieve its increased performance, the craft sacrifices armor, deflector shields, hyperdrive systems, and life-support: pilots must rely on their skills and superior numbers to survive.

Lethal Adversary Veteran rebel pilots know not to underestimate the deadly speed and maneuverability of the TIE interceptor.

INNOVATIVE DESIGN

To maximize speed for the TIE interceptor, Imperial designers increased the size of the standard twin ion engines and provided the necessary additional power input by increasing the size of the solar panels. Designers also utilized the "bent-wing" configuration of Darth Vader's prototype TIE fighter, but reshaped the side panels to create dagger-shaped wings that give the pilot a wider field of view from the cockpit.

Cutaway wing design makes craft lighter and provides improved lateral pilot vision

Angled solar-wing creates smaller target profile

Sensor packages

Pilot

Advanced targeting sensors

Transparisteel viewport

Wing-tip blaster cannons

Mounts for additional laser cannons (optional)

Energy accumulator conduits

Ultra-high efficiency girondium-colium solar cells

Increased Firepower Unlike the twin chin-mounted lasers found on the TIE fighter, the interceptor has four cannons on the tips of its solar arrays.

LEGACY OF A BOUNTY HUNTER

After the bounty hunter Jango Fett died at the Battle of Geonosis, his son Boba fled in his father's ship, *Slave I*, and almost immediately began plotting his revenge. He also began working as a bounty hunter, and used his profits to maintain and refurbish *Slave I*. Despite his youth and limited experience, he became the leader of a group of hunters, most of whom were more than twice his age. By the end of the Clone Wars, he had gained a professional reputation in his own right.

"Put Captain Solo in the cargo hold."

Boba Fett

Boba Fett in pilot position

Repulsorlifts in the "wings" lift the ship away from gravity sources

Concealed concussion missile launcher

Hidden homing beacon launcher

FLIGHT ATTITUDE

For maximum pilot visibility and most effective weapons use, *Slave I* flies in a vertical attitude. The unusual configuration requires unorthodox piloting skills, which Boba Fett learned at an early age by watching his father, Jango. *Slave I* is built more for stealth, defense, and attack than for speed, but with maximum power diverted to the main drives the ship can match the space velocities of a Y-wing starfighter.

Illegal Technology *Slave I*'s sensor jamming and masking system originated as a highly classified experimental project for the Imperial Navy, and enables Fett to closely pursue other ships across space while remaining invisible on their sensors.

SLAVE I

Boba Fett's distinctive starship was already heavily modified to suit the needs of a professional bounty hunter when he inherited the vessel from his father, Jango Fett. However, Boba undertook additional upgrades of his own. *Slave I* is crammed tight with auxiliary sensor systems of every kind, heavy-duty shield generators, and several added weapons systems. A stolen military secret sensor jamming and masking device enables *Slave I* to disappear from most scanning systems. Its manifold capabilities make it one of Boba Fett's most dangerous assets as he tracks his quarry across the galaxy.

Pilot's seat

Tracking system monitor

As *Slave I* comes in to land, the cockpit capsule rotates to keep Boba Fett and any passengers upright

Sensor array

Flight computers

Armor plate

Cockpit energy shield

Power cell monitors

Cargo hold

Sensor jamming unit

Fuel monitors

Fuel baffles

Tachyon emission detector

Communications monitor

Passive long-range sensor bands

Interference shielding

High-power rectenna

Receptor boost energizer

Magnetic tuning antenna

Dymek concussion missiles are used to disable opponents' shield generators

Main engine

Power generator

Passenger seat

DESIGNED TO DECEIVE

Slave I hides most of its weapons to appear lightly armed, exposing only its short-range twin blaster cannons. The ship's appearance encourages opponents to underestimate *Slave I* until it is too late.

168

Hidden panels conceal the ship's powerful ion cannon

Pilot's sleeping quarters

Tractor beam generator

Static discharge port

Weapons control systems

Spinal trunk line carries data from ship systems and weapons to main computer

Short-range twin blaster cannons

Life support

Access crawlway

Composite tractor beam projector in extensible turret

Laser generator

Proton torpedoes, concealed by hidden panels, deploy to either side

Outer plating

Han Solo encased in carbonite

Anti-ionization mesh

Radiator fins

Deflector generator

Boba Fett is about to raise the cockpit capsule to make room for Han to be stored in the cargo hold

Power generator

Stabilizing field projector

Prisoner cages

Wing extension struts

Repulsorlifts rotate to maintain support for ship as it comes in to land on its back

WEAPONS

Boba Fett has used the overwhelming weaponry of *Slave I* to ruthlessly destroy the heavily armed craft of enemies and rival bounty hunters. He has reduced even gunboats to blasted hulks before they can respond, as the ship's hidden weapons systems allow it to launch devastating surprise attacks that strain the four on-board power generators to the maximum. *Slave I*'s tractor beams catch and hold small craft for destruction or boarding, and allow Boba Fett to "latch on" to more powerful ships, making the bounty hunter virtually inescapable.

PRISON SHIP

While Boba Fett is notorious for disintegrating those whom he has been hired to kill, some bounties require that the quarry be brought back alive. Accordingly, *Slave I* is equipped with prisoner cages, with six immobilizing bunks.

Valuable Cargo Frozen in carbonite, Han Solo is transferred to *Slave I*'s cargo hold for transport to Jabba the Hutt, who will reward Fett with a bounty of 250,000 credits.

VITAL ASSET

The limited resources of the Rebel Alliance mean that, wherever possible, ships have to be operationally flexible and able to perform multiple roles. In addition to its medical facilities, the *Redemption*'s other features include extremely sophisticated scanners and a powerful deep-space, multi-frequency antenna, making the vessel more than adequate as a battle command base.

COMBAT HOSPITAL

Unlike the Empire, the Rebel Alliance puts a high priority on the availability of medical attention at the site of conflict. The *Redemption* travels with the rebel fleet, often directly into combat situations. However, the *Redemption*'s status as a hospital ship gives it no special protection from Imperial forces, who regard any rebel as a legitimate target, even those who are wounded. Every medical droid aboard *Redemption* is programmed to treat trauma patients. For patients who have suffered the loss of limbs, 2-1B surgical droids use diagnostic computers and genetic reconstruction tools to create cybernetic prosthetics with tactile sensitivity.

Forward tractor beam projector

Upper turbolaser turret

Primary communication array

Short range communications array

Fresh water tanks

Auxiliary power generator

Laboratory with pathogen analysis and containment facilities

Recovery ward

Intensive-care units

Patient rooms

Officers' quarters

Passenger quarters

Bacta tanks

Main bridge with raised command platform

Surgery suite viewport

Morgue

Cargo bay

Recycling systems

Forward sensor array

Aft sensor array

Main turbolaser

Main laser cannon

MEDICAL FRIGATE

The Alliance's hospital ship *Redemption* is a converted EF76 Nebulon-B Imperial escort frigate, which originally featured 12 turbolaser batteries, 12 laser cannons, and hangars for two squadrons of TIE fighters. The Alliance removed most of the frigate's weapons and replaced them with back-up systems for power generators and shield projectors. The frigate's standard starfighter launch bay configuration was transformed into a hospital facility that can treat over 700 patients simultaneously. Equipped with intensive-care units, operating theaters, recovery wards, numerous medical droids, and 16 bacta tanks, the ship's patient-survival rate is nearly 98 percent.

Propulsion Module The rear end of the Nebulon-B's propulsion module has an array of seven Galaxy-15 ion engines. Though not as fast as other ships, the *Redemption*'s importance as a hospital ship places it among the fleet's most valued.

Engineering boom

Delphus JC-671 deflector shield generator

Chief engineer's quarters

Main engineering operations center

Titanium-reinforced alloy hull

Docking tube (retracted)—can accommodate starfighters or transport vessels

Galaxy-15 ion engine reactor (one of seven)

Hyperdrive generator

Static discharge vein

Power cells

Ion drive thruster nozzle

Surgery Suite After Luke Skywalker is injured in a lightsaber duel with Darth Vader, the medical droid 2-1B treats Luke's wounded arm in a surgery suite aboard the *Redemption*.

FORMER WARSHIP

Kuat Drive Yards produced Nebulon-B frigates for the Imperial Navy, which used the vessels to escort Imperial supply convoys across hyperspace lanes. Although slower and less maneuverable than the Corellian Corvettes previously used for Imperial escort duty, Nebulon-Bs were equipped with heavy firepower to deal with large attackers, and were less expensive than Star Destroyers. Several Nebulon-Bs have defected to or been captured by the rebels.

HOME ONE

Originally a deep-space exploration ship constructed by Mon Calamari Shipyards, the MC80 Star Cruiser *Home One* has been extensively modified for war against the Empire. Thousands of viewports that once virtually covered the ship's exterior have been covered with heavy armor plating. Hangars for small shuttles were expanded to carry squadrons of starfighters. Standard defensive weaponry for eliminating asteroid obstacles were replaced with turbolaser batteries, ion cannon batteries, and tractor beam emitters capable of snaring enemy starfighters. *Home One* famously served as Admiral Ackbar's command vessel for the attack on the second Death Star at the Battle of Endor.

Command Center On the bridge of *Home One*, Admiral Ackbar gives instructions to his Mon Calamari crew as he leads them into battle.

Main shuttle integrates with ship and transports personnel to and from planets

Main bridge and briefing area

Cargo modules

Docking clamp

Umbilicals link shuttle to ship's primary systems

Main reactor

Reactor/ hyperdrive interface

Hyperdrive generator

Hyperdrive field emitter

Ion injection manifold

Escape pods

Starboard thrusters

Starboard main sublight ion engines

DISTINCTIVE CONTROLS

Various species from across the galaxy make up the rebel personnel on *Home One*, but due to the design of the ship's controls, the command crew is exclusively made up of Mon Calamari. Holo-displays and battle graphics are designed specifically for the Mon Calamari, who do not see in the same spectrum as humans. So long as Admiral Ackbar and his crew are at the controls, however, the Alliance trusts their fleet is in good hands.

REBEL RETROFIT

Like most Mon Calamari cruisers, *Home One* was originally designed with numerous water-filled passage tubes that snaked throughout the ship's interior, allowing the Mon Calamari crew to swim to different areas of the ship. To accommodate non-amphibious rebel crewmembers, various tubes were drained and retrofitted with flooring, stairs, and ventilation.

DETACHABLE SHIPS

Mon Calamari engineers modified *Home One* with detachable sections that can function as independent ships for attack or escape. Despite this modification, Admiral Ackbar prefers to keep his command vessel's parts united.

Secondary passenger shuttle

Forward sensors and communications

Central atrium with artificial environment of water and vegetation overlooked by accommodation suites

Upper deflector shield protector array

Turbolasers

Tractor beam emitter

Atmosphere ducts distribute processed air to all parts of ship

Forward crew spaces

Starboard lateral deflector array

Main atmospheric processing plant can produce breathable atmospheres for many different species and distribute to various zones via atmosphere ducts

Elevator to lower hangar

Hangar atmosphere force field

Millennium Falcon

Imperial shuttle

Port and starboard hangar connection tunnel

X-Wings

"May the Force be with us."
Admiral Ackbar

MON CALAMARI DESIGN

Although no two Mon Calamari vessels are precisely alike, nearly all resemble elongated, bulbous cylinders and appear organic, as if they were grown rather than built. Each is designed to meet Mon Calamari standards for efficiency, structural strength, and aesthetic appeal. Mon Calamari cruisers are covered with pods, bulges, and bumps arranged in a seemingly haphazard pattern, which contain sensor arrays, recessed weapon batteries, shield generators, and observation decks.

Deflector shield generator

Starboard hangar entrance

Main power conduits run the length of the ship

Ventral shield projector vanes

Escape pod exit

Lower hangar bay

Atmosphere duct

Composite deflector blister

Strange Pairing The rebel fleet consists of a disparate variety of ships, but a YT-1300 smuggling ship and a stolen Imperial shuttle make an especially unusual pair inside one of *Home One*'s hangars.

173

Reactor
heat sink

Waste conduits
remove heat
and radiation
from reactor

Neuranium/
lanthanide
reactor shielding

Main power-
reactor for
spacecraft
systems

Cabin in
passenger
configuration
with seating for
20 passengers

Rebel strike
team prepare
for the assault
on Endor

Rear
gun-turret
power feed

Retractable blaster

Rear defensive
twin-blaster turret

Starboard hyperdrive
field projector

Port wing

Starboard hyperdrive
field generator

Sublight
ion engine
nozzle

Ion engine
thrust
chamber

Hyperdrive-
unit power
converter

Sublight ion engine

Ion engine fuel tanks

Shield generator power cells

ALLIANCE ASSAULT

When it first rolled off the Sienar production line, the *Lambda*-class shuttle
Tydirium was used for Imperial courier and transport duties in the Prefsbelt
system. After the Battle of Hoth, Alliance pilot "Ace" Azzameen secured
Imperial codes for the *Tydirium* from an orbital outpost in the Zhar system.
Wedge Antilles then led a daring rebel raid on Prefsbelt to liberate the vehicle
for the Alliance. Using the codes stolen by Azzameen, the *Tydirium* was employed
to penetrate the Imperial defenses around the forest moon of Endor, and land a
strike team to deactivate the shield generator protecting the second Death Star.

IMPERIAL SHUTTLE

Renowned for its reliability, the *Lambda*-class T-4a shuttle is one of the most widely used vessels in the Imperial fleet. Its primary function is to transfer personnel and cargo between the Empire's capital ships, but it is also used for planetary landings and ship-to-ship transfers between smaller Imperial vessels. A versatile craft, the shuttle is capable of being configured in several versions—as a cargo carrier, troop ship, courier vessel, or diplomatic transport. Many Imperial officials use the T-4a shuttle as a personal transport, as its armaments, heavily reinforced hull, and shielding enable it to travel in safety, even without a military escort—the Emperor himself uses a highly modified *Lambda*-class vessel. The shuttle's distinctive tri-wing design enables it to function in both space and planetary atmospheres. On landing, the heavily shielded lower wings fold upward to protect the ship's occupants.

Reinforced blast-door to seal bulkhead in the event cockpit is used as an escape craft

C-3PO

Han Solo

Chewbacca

Gunner's station

Forward scanner array

Leia Organa

Luke Skywalker

R2-D2

Flight engineer's station

Fixed-position offensive laser cannons

Twin rotating long-range blasters

Starboard retro-thrust engine

Retro-thrust engine fuel cells

Blaster power-feed

Blaster rotation mechanism

Landing-gear extension jacks

Starboard landing gear

Deflector shield generator heat-sink

Starboard-wing deflector shield projector

Starboard-wing deflector shield generator

Power feeds for deflector shield projectors

Main wing structural support beam

Covert Mission
Piloted by Han Solo and Chewbacca, and carrying a rebel strike force, the Lambda-class shuttle *Tydirium* arrives in the Imperial-occupied Endor system.

MULTIPLE MANUFACTURERS

Designed by Sienar Fleet Systems, the standard version of the T-4a shuttle is one of the manufacturer's most popular lines. In addition to Imperial contracts for the T-4a, the shuttle is also in great demand by many planetary governments and some of the galaxy's wealthiest individuals. To fulfill orders for a heavily armed, military version of the shuttle, technological genius Raith Sienar subcontracted production of the variant to Cygnus Spaceworks. However, this rival manufacturer has since tried to compete with Sienar by producing a non-military model that is almost identical to the standard T-4a design.

EMERGENCY LIFEBOAT

In the event that the *Lambda*-class T-4a is disabled, the cockpit can be jettisoned from the main body of the vehicle and used to travel a short distance at sublight speed. The cockpit, however, is not large enough to carry the shuttle's full complement of 20 passengers—on Imperial craft, priority for a place on the lifeboat is given to the most senior personnel on board.

Rocket thrusters propel cockpit at sublight speed

Wings badly damaged by rebel laser fire

Passenger cabin abandoned as cockpit executes emergency separation

JABBA'S SAIL BARGE

Jabba the Hutt's sail barge *Khetanna* represents a strange combination of opulence and crude minimalism, befitting the tastes of its vile owner. The giant pleasure craft floats on repulsorlifts, carrying the crime lord from his palace in the Tatooine wastes to his Mos Eisley estate and back again. Jabba is also known to take the *Khetanna* sailing far across the Dune Sea to conduct dark negotiations, or to attend distant high-stakes races that contribute to his gambling empire. Its most nefarious purposes have involved conveying the Hutt to scenes of execution, or to violent and deadly gladiatorial combats staged for his entertainment in remote desert valleys. Wherever it is seen, the barge brings the ominous shadow of its master's presence.

Observation Lounge Enjoying libations inside his barge's spacious observation lounge, Jabba commands his minions to dispose of a group of prisoners while a captive Princess Leia and C-3PO look on.

Sail support structure

Enlarged kitchen

Lead lookout

Guest rooms

Navigation monitors

Flight console

Cockpit security

Navigation sensor array

Power cells

Decorative hull plating

Prisoners and others forced to fight and die for Jabba's entertainment are pushed to combat or death from the skiffs

Terrain sensor

Han, Chewie, and Luke—Jabba's prisoners

Lando Calrissian in disguise

Communications antenna

Prison cell

Lead lookout

Skiff controls

Live food tank

Steering vane

Repulsor cooling vents

SAND SKIFFS

Two sand skiffs accompany the *Khetanna* on its journeys. These repulsorlift skimmers ferry passengers to and from the sail barge. En route, the small craft carry guards and watchmen on the lookout for ambush by any of Jabba's many enemies. The skiffs are hardly more than flying platforms—uncomfortable and unprotected from wind, sand, or sun—and are meant to give the guards a clear view of everything around them.

Forward sail

R2-D2

Custom-mounted deck gun

C-3PO

Princess Leia

Boba Fett

Aft sail

Aft lookout

Privacy lounge, used by Jabba's most favored guests and lieutenants

Ventilation grate

Adjustable shutters

Jabba the Hutt: Jabba boards the barge via a large hatch at observation deck level

Max Rebo

Bib Fortuna

Thrust exhausts

Decorative bas-relief

Access hatch

Thrust monitors

Aft divans

A variety of guests, criminal conspirators, henchmen, hired killers, and other undesirables accompany Jabba on voyages

The observation lounge, where Jabba enjoys watching his prisoners' last moments

Triple thrust turbines carry the barge efficiently across long distances

Main engine

Engine sensor

Thrust chamber

Power generator heat vent

Power converter

Power generator

Armory

Steering control linkage

Maintenance walkway

Repulsor generator

Repulsor coils

Steering repulsor

Steering vane

Decorative finial

Engineer's corridor

JABBA'S PLEASURES

While other such expensive leisure craft are fitted out with luxuries of every kind, the *Khetanna* is mostly bare metal. Its main luxury is an elaborate kitchen: Jabba's appetites for pleasures of the flesh include an average of nine meals a day, keeping his food preparers busy at all times. The barge also holds tanks for the live food that Jabba often prefers.

SAILING THE DUNE SEA

Archaeological evidence suggests Tatooine's Dune Sea was once an actual sea, but the punishing heat of the planet's twin suns evaporated the waters long ago. Now, the terrain consists of rolling dunes and trackless wastes, dotted with the occasional remains of dead creatures and crashed starships. Yet to some brave and foolhardy inhabitants of Tatooine, the Dune Sea is not a place to be avoided, but actually an opportunity for travel, utilizing sail barges like Jabba the Hutt's *Khetanna*. These look rather like primitive wind-driven craft, but in fact the decorative sails are most important as awnings, shading those on deck from the glare of Tatooine's twin suns. The sails can and do propel barges in moderate winds, but primary propulsion is provided by conventional thrust systems.

Double Duty Traveling alongside Jabba's sail barge, the skiff's crew serves not only as guards for Jabba's prisoners, but as lookouts for Tusken snipers who may be hiding in the surrounding dunes.

Deck Gun Put in place to protect Jabba, the sail barge's deck gun ultimately becomes its destroyer, when Princess Leia fires it through the top deck.

ARMED LUXURY

The *Khetanna* was designed long ago as a pleasure vehicle, and was never meant to be armed. Jabba's activities have brought him under attack more than once, however, and the Dune Sea is a dangerous place, so armament modifications were made to the barge at his palace workshops. The handrails were drilled to provide fittings for portable heavy blasters, and a powerful deck gun was installed to disable attacking vehicles. This gun has also been used to destroy the dwellings of those on Tatooine who oppose or displease Jabba.

Sail Barge Wreck Following its destruction at the hands of Luke Skywalker and his companions, the wreck of Jabba's sail barge joins the countless others dotting the Dune Sea.

FAST AND DANGEROUS

After Imperial forces decided to build a massive shield generator on Endor's forest moon to protect the second Death Star, they initially utilized AT-STs and AT-ATs for reconnaissance of the cleared areas surrounding the generator. However, because the moon's thick underbrush and dense woodland terrain made most Imperial vehicles impractical, the bulk of the vehicular patrol duty was handled by Imperial scout troopers riding explosively fast Aratech 74-Z speeder bikes.

Modified Guidance Systems
Speeder bikes on Endor were equipped with an extra sensor plate added on to the front control vanes.

Forest Patrol Although the tall Endor trees presented a definite hazard to speeder bikes, the forest was crisscrossed by numerous trails that scout troopers could traverse safely.

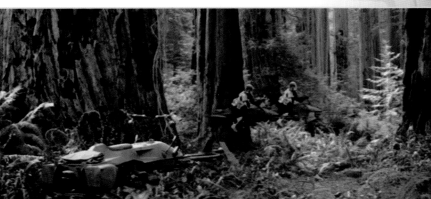

Blaster Cannon The 74-Z speeder bike is armed with a rotating blaster cannon located under the chassis. The cannon's controls are on the bike's handlebars.

Rapid Deceleration Although modified guidance systems gave troopers a much clearer idea of the terrain and obstacles beyond the trees immediately ahead of them, in combat, mistakes were easily made.

High speed
steering vanes

Multi scanner
array

Universal handgrips
are engineered to allow
single-handed operation

Blaster cannon
firing controls

Steering
sensitivity
adjust

Tracking
sensor/comlink

Power
management
settings

Sensor settings

Seat
cushion

Outriggers built
to withstand
extreme torque

BlasTech Ax-20
blaster cannon can
fire repeated blasts
without overheating

Rotating
mount

Steering
linkages

Guidance system
electronics

Laser cannon
power coupling

Power
converter

Structural
bracing

Fuel cell is
self-charging

Fuel line

Power cell
rechargers

Laser power
cells

Repulsor
block

Power plant

Rocker-pivoted
footpad controls
speed and altitude

Pursuit Vehicle On Endor's Forest Moon, an Imperial scout gives chase to a rebel agent. The scout's helmet has a built-in sensor to scan a 180-degree area while flying close to the ground.

74-Z HISTORY

Manufactured by the over-4,000-year-old Aratech Repulsor Company, the 74-Z speeder bike has been in production for decades. The model used by Imperial scouts remains essentially the same as those used by the Galactic Army during the Clone Wars. Design variations include 74-Zs adapted specifically for hot and cold environments, and also high-altitude versions for mountainous regions.

SCOUT SPEEDER BIKE

The Aratech 74-Z speeder bike is a small, one-man repulsorlift vehicle, and is the core equipment of an Imperial scout troop. Used to perform reconnaissance, perimeter defense, patrol missions in cooperation with AT-ST walkers, and surgical strikes against small enemy forces, the explosively quick vehicle is far more maneuverable than landspeeders or airspeeders. In addition, it allows the Imperial military to establish and maintain a tangible presence across vast areas of occupied worlds. The 74-Z has a self-charging energy source that allows a scout to explore and patrol far from base without worrying about fuel capacity. Speeder bikes are armed with small blaster cannons and are lightly armored for added protection.

Tractor seat systems keep rider in place

Inertial compensator

Heat exchanger

Tarp for wilderness shelter

High-strength actuator for repulsor deflector

Repulsor projection unit (multi-directional)

Thrust array

Repulsor deflector (air brake)

Versatile Controls Although the 74-Z is designed for Imperial scouts of average height, the controls can be operated by a variety of riders.

SPEEDER CONTROLS

The bike is manipulated by handlebar and foot pedal controls that move four small directional steering vanes on twin outriggers that extend from the front of the bike. Elevation and direction are determined through the use of two handgrips, located at the shoulder level in front of the pilot. Speed controls built into rocker-pivoted footpads provide maximum acceleration, while the saddle section houses levers and knobs used for parking, weaponry settings, and communications.

RZ-1 A-WING

The small, wedge-shaped RZ-1 A-wing was one of the Rebel Alliance's most daring innovations during the Galactic Civil War. Created in response to the Empire's profusion of TIE fighters and their variants, the A-wing was designed to be the fastest starfighter in the galaxy. The sleek ship sacrifices shields, heavy weapons, and hull armor for speed and lightning-fast acceleration. The craft is ideally suited to hit-and-run missions, surgical strikes on capital ships, long-range patrols, and reconnaissance and intelligence-gathering missions. Its twin stabilizers and control surfaces also enable it to operate effectively as an atmospheric fighter. Derived from the Tammuzan's sleek R-22 *Spearhead* starfighter, the A-wing was designed by General Jan Dodonna, with assistance from rebel engineer Walex Blissex. The A-wing was constructed in the utmost secrecy before the Battle of Endor, where it displayed its deadly value as a strike craft.

INTELLIGENCE GATHERER

The hyperdrive capability, speed, and maneuverability of the A-wing make it ideal for intelligence-gathering and reconnaissance missions. An experienced A-wing pilot can drop out of hyperspace close to an Imperial fleet or space-installation, and make a blistering run around it (or even through a fleet, if the flier is daring enough). Using concealed multi-spectral imagers and other sensors, the pilot is able to gather information and escape back into hyperspace before TIE fighters can be scrambled. The A-wing's intelligence-gathering and strike capabilities are enhanced by its powerful sensor-jamming system, which can disrupt the detection and targeting systems of TIE fighters and other small vessels. However, this equipment is not so effective against capital ships as their sensors are more complex. The A-wing's jamming system can also endanger the craft when directed at a larger vessel, as its powerful broadcasts can be detected to reveal the starfighter's exact position to the enemy.

Corrugated carbo-plas provides structural strength with light weight

Concealed multi-spectral holographic imager for reconnaissance missions

Deflector shield generator

Deflector shield projector

Thruster control jets (located under cowling above reactor exhaust)

Adjustable stabilizer acts as control surface during atmospheric flight

Fusion reactor exhaust

Emergency datalog for reconnaissance intelligence information (can be ejected if craft is in danger of capture or destruction)

Thrust vector control

Green Leader
Rebel pilot Arvel Crynyd flew under the call sign "Green Leader" at the Battle of Endor, where he led the pilots who made up Green Squadron, and helped destroy Darth Vader's flagship, the *Executor*.

LAST RESORT

The A-wing typically relies on its exceptional speed to evade attack or pursuit, but, in the event that a pilot cannot escape, the craft provides one last-resort option. The wedge-shaped prow is fitted with a reinforced heat shield for atmospheric entry, which can also act as an effective "battering ram" at close range in atmospheric flight. In space battles, an A-wing pilot with no hope of escape or survival might choose to ram an enemy vessel, relying on the nose wedge to breach the ship's hull and destroy it.

Advanced
avionics
system

Targeting computer
holographic display
projector

Sensor
power-jamming
array

Maintenance
diagnostic
system

Maintenance
access hatch

Targeting
computer
system

Reinforced
front wedge
(can be used
to ram enemy
vessels)

Forward
sensor array

Concussion
missile in flight

Thrust-vector control pedal

Concussion-missile magazine
(holds a total of 6 missiles)

Starboard concussion-missile launcher

Sublight engine throttle (controls
engine thrust and velocity)

Starboard gyro-
stabilizing unit

Laser
cannon

Low-power
targeting laser

Laser cannon
swivel
mounting

Transparisteel
cockpit canopy

On-board
systems
waste-heat
radiators

Life-support
systems

Pilot

Novaldex
"Event Horizon"
sublight
engines

STING IN THE TAIL

Although the A-wing is only lightly armed, its
weaponry still packs a powerful punch. The ship
is fitted with two laser cannons, fixed to unique
swivel mounts that enable the cannons to fire in
a 120° arc (60° above and below the horizontal).
In addition, these mounts can be modified to allow
the lasers to pivot and fire behind the ship while it
is still racing forward. More than one TIE pilot has
met an unexpected fate after dropping onto an
A-wing's tail with the impression that the ship was
a sitting target. While enhancing the A-wing's chances
of survival, the weapons mount has a high rate
of mechanical failure and contributes to
the craft's extremely high maintenance-
to-flight ratio, which makes it difficult
to keep a squadron of A-wings
operational for any length of time.

Durasteel
hull

Fusion
reactor
exhaust

Starboard landing
gear (in retracted
position)

The A-wing fighter has an extremely
sensitive control system—only the very
best pilots are capable of handling the
craft with ease

Fusion
reactors

Hyperdrive generator
cooling matrix
(hyperdrive generator
located behind matrix)

183

SWIVEL-WING STARFIGHTER

The B-wing has a unique design in which the cockpit remains fixed in regard to the plane of travel, while the gyroscopically mounted main wing can pivot around it, swiveling through 360°. This enables the entire wing assembly to swing from side to side horizontally and vertically, providing a wider arc of weapons' fire. This motion also changes the sensor-reflection configuration of the vessel, making it a much harder target to hit. While the B-wing's design and capabilities enhance the ship's tactical value, they also make it a difficult craft to fly, both in space combat and in atmospheric operations. Only the most skilled pilots can handle the B-wing—these fighter aces tend to become attached to their ships and supervise every repair and modification.

Blue Squadron At the Battle of Endor, the Rebel Alliance's Blue Squadron includes A-wings as well as B-wings. This unusual combination comes about in part because relatively few rebel pilots have sufficient training to operate B-wings.

CUSTOMIZED FIREPOWER

The B-wing's formidable firepower is enhanced by its versatility. Each of its eight weapon-mounting points can be reconfigured with various combinations of armaments for specific missions, or to suit the particular preferences of the pilot. The standard B-wing configuration features three ion cannons, two auto-blasters, and two proton torpedo launchers, but alternate weapons configurations include variants with three laser cannons and up to four auto-blasters. The wing-tip weapon emplacements can also be substituted with other equipment modules to configure the B-wing for noncombat duties. After the Battle of Endor, several B-wings were fitted with flame-retardant projectors by Alliance technicians so that the craft could be utilized for fire-fighting purposes.

Ion cannon

Low-power laser for precision targeting of ion cannon

S-foil wing in deployed position

Cooling-system intake

Long-range forward scanners

Main sensor array

Mount point for additional auto-blaster or other weapon (optional configuration)

Low-power targeting laser

Twin auto-blasters

Weather radar

Short-range tactical sensor array

Main targeting computer

Deflector-shield generator

Proton torpedo warhead magazine

Secondary proton torpedo launcher (with armored port-cover closed)

Main heat radiators

Port nacelle housing fore- and aft-deflector-shield projectors (obscured)

Retro thrust nozzles

Inertial compensator

Pilot (Ten Numb)

Transparisteel canopy

Cockpit gyrostabilizing system

Life-support systems

Escape pod sublight engine

Starboard nacelle housing fore and aft deflector-shield projectors

Engine thrust nozzle (one of four)

Reactor for single engine feeding four thrust chambers

Hyperdrive projector (hyperdrive generator located behind projector)

Reactor excess-plasma vent

High-power energy cell supplying anti-gravity generator

Anti-gravity generator

Repulsorlift projectors

Field-transportable maintenance computer

Refueling pump and fuel-monitoring system

Main maintenance diagnostic-systems workstation

transparent to electromagnetic waves]

Torpedo launcher recharge cylinder

Proton torpedo warhead magazine showing 3 warheads (magazine carries 4 in total)

Heavy laser cannon

Low-power targeting laser

Primary proton torpedo launcher, with torpedo in firing position (launch doors open)

Ion cannon (uses low-power laser associated with adjacent laser cannon for precision targeting)

Ion charge generator

Torpedo launch tube recharge pipes

Velocity sensors

Structural beam

Wing status sensors

Primary wing

Navigation sensor array

Ion cannon

Low-power precision-targeting laser

Jammer system for scrambling enemy sensors

Jammer control unit

Spinal power trunk

S-foil wing actuator system

DESIGN DRAWBACKS

The complex design of the B-wing means that fighters require longer, more frequent maintenance periods than most other Alliance vessels. They are difficult to service because their "parked" configuration stacks all three wings on top of each other, making access to the central area awkward. The main wing's gyro-mechanism is also prone to in-flight failure: fighters are "frozen" in their wing configuration at the moment of failure, which leads to maneuvering problems.

B-WING

Conceived as a replacement for the Y-wing, the B-wing heavy assault starfighter is one of the Rebellion's most well-armed warcraft, playing a key role at the Battle of Endor. Personally designed by Commander (now Admiral) Ackbar with the help of Verpine engineers, the B-wing packs firepower equal to an Imperial Corvette—though at a much lower construction price. The ship's primary role is as an attack vessel targeting the Empire's capital ships. It also escorts X- and Y-wing fighter squadrons and Alliance convoys, and can be deployed for assaults on space-based or planetary-surface Imperial facilities. The starfighter is essentially a long wing with a pair of folding S-foils, and it boasts a formidable array of weapons, including ion cannons and proton torpedo launchers. These armaments are linked to the ship's advanced targeting computer for coordinated precision strikes, with the assistance of low-power targeting lasers. The B-wing's arsenal can be computer-controlled for coordinated fire, or independently targeted by the pilot. The craft also has a unique cockpit design—the pilot remains stationary while the rest of the ship rotates during flight. In the event that the B-wing is seriously damaged, the cockpit can also serve as an emergency escape pod.

VEHICLE TECHNICAL DATA

REPUBLIC CRUISER

Manufacturer: Corellian Engineering Corporation
Make: Space Cruiser
Length: 115 m (380 ft)
Sublight engines: 3 Dyne 577 radial atomizers

Hyperdrive: Longe Voltrans tri-arc CD-3.2
Crew: 8 (captain, 2 co-pilots, 2 communications officers, 3 engineers)
Passenger capacity: 16
Armament: None (unarmed diplomatic vessel)
Escape pods: two 8-person pods plus salon pod

SEBULBA'S PODRACER

Engine manufacturer/type: Collor Pondrat Plug-F Mammoth racing engines, fitted with Split-X ram air/radiator intakes
Engine length: 7.47 m (24½ ft)
Max. speed: 829 kph (515 mph)
Max. repulsorlift altitude: 85 m (275 ft)
Fuel: Tradium power fluid pressurized with quold runium, activated with ionized injectrine

ANAKIN'S PODRACER

Engine manufacturer/type: Radon-Ulzer 620C racing engines, modified heavily by Anakin Skywalker
Engine length: 7 m (23 ft)
Max. speed: estimated 947 kph (588 mph)
Max. repulsorlift altitude: 105 m (350 ft)
Fuel: straight Tradium power fluid activated with injectrine, no additives

LANDING SHIP

Design and manufacture: Haor Chall Engineering
Wingspan: 370 m (1,200 ft)
Hyperdrive: none
Max. atmospheric speed: 587 kph (365 mph)
Troop carrier capacity: 7 per wing; total 28
AAT (Armored Assault Tank) capacity: 24 per fore wing, 33 per aft wing; total 114
MTT (Multi-Troop Transport) capacity: 3 per fore wing, 3 in stage area, 2 in landing pedestal; total 11
Crew: 88 (droids only)
Armament: 2 pairs of wing-tip laser cannons, 4 turret-mounted cannons

MTT

Design and manufacture: Baktoid Armor Workshop
Troop capacity: 112 battle droids carrying standard blaster rifles
Armament: four 17 kv anti-personnel blasters twin-mounted in ball turrets
Length: 31 m (103 ft)
Height: 13 m (43 ft)
Max. ground speed: 35 kph (22 mph)
Max. lift altitude: 4 m (13 ft)
Deployment method: carried to planet surface in C-9979 landing ship

GUNGAN SUB

Design and manufacture: Otoh Gunga Bongameken Cooperative
Make: tribubble bongo sub
Length: 15 m (50 ft)
Cargo capacity: 800 kg (1800 lb) in each of 2 cargo bubbles
Crew: 1 (with 2 passengers)
Special features: the forward cockpit can eject as an escape pod in emergencies, but can sustain its hydrostatic field only briefly, so it must race for the surface before its power runs out

SITH INFILTRATOR

Manufacturer: Sienar Design Systems, later customized in a secret laboratory

Make: armed star courier rebuilt as a unique 2-deck Sith Infiltrator

Length: 26.5 m (88 ft)

Sublight drive: high-temperature X-C 2 ion drive array

Hyperdrive: Sienar SSDS 11-A (class 3.0)

Crew: 1, with capacity for 6 passengers

Primary armament: 6 low-profile laser cannons (4 original, 2 added)

DROID STARFIGHTER

Design and manufacture: Xi Char cathedral factories, Charros IV

Length: 3.5 m (12 ft) wing tip to wing tip

Crew: permanent automated droid brain controlled by remote signal

Armament: 4 blaster cannons, 2 energy torpedo launchers

Flight time before refueling: 35 minutes

DROID CONTROL SHIP

Design and manufacture: Hoersch-Kessel Drive, Inc. (primary contractor)

Diameter: 3,170 m (10,400 ft)

Sublight engines: Rendili stardrive proton 2 (primary)/ proton 12 (secondary)

Droid control signal max. safe broadcast range: 16,500 km (10,300 miles)

Droid starfighter max. capacity: 1,500 fighters

C-9979 landing ship max. load: 25 per cargo arm; total 50

MTT (Multi-Troop Transport) max. load: 550

AAT (Armored Assault Tank) max. load: 6,250

Troop carrier max. load: 1,500

Armament: 42 quad laser emplacements

NABOO N-1 STARFIGHTER

Design and manufacture: Spaceframe by Theed Palace Space Vessel Engineering Corps

Configuration: J-type (twin radial sublight engines)

Length: 11 m (36 ft)

Sublight engines: Nubian 221, modified

Hyperdrive: Nubian Monarc C-4

Crew: 1 pilot, assisted by 1 mandatory astromech droid

Armament: twin laser cannons; proton torpedo magazine with capacity of 10 torpedoes

AAT

Design and manufacture: Baktoid Armor Workshop

Make: AAT (Armored Assault Tank)

Length: 9.75 m (32 ft)

Max. speed: 55 kph (35 mph)

Crew: 4 battle droids (commander, pilot, 2 gunners)

Armament: primary turret laser cannon; twin lateral range-finding lasers; twin lateral antipersonnel lasers; 6 energy shell projectile launchers

FLASH SPEEDER

Length: 4.5 m (14½ ft)
Crew: 1
Passengers: 1
Armament: 1 laser blaster

GIAN SPEEDER

Length: 5.7 m (18½ ft)
Crew: 1 pilot, 1 gunner
Passengers: 2
Armament: 3 laser blasters

CORUSCANT TAXI

Length: 8 m (25 ft)
Top speed: 191 kph (115 mph)
Max. altitude: 3.4 km (2.1 miles)
Normal max. trip range: 210 km (131 miles)
Crew: 1
Passengers: depends on species
Armament: none

NABOO CRUISER

Manufacturer: Theed Palace Space Vessel Engineering Corps
Make: J-type custom-built diplomatic barge
Dimensions: length 39 m (128 ft); width 91 m (298.5 ft); depth 6.8 m (22.3 ft)
Max. speed (in standard atmosphere): 2,000 kph (1,240 mph)
Max. acceleration (in space): 2,500G
Power: main reactor peak $3x10^{12}$ megawatts; peak shielding $6x10^{12}$ megawatts
Hyperdrive: Nubian 288 cores; S-6 generators (class 0.7; range 80,000 light years fully fuelled)
Crew: 1 pilot; 1 co-pilot; 3 others optional (navigator/comscan/ shield operator); 5 astromech droids
Passengers: 4 prestige passengers; 6 guards
Armament: none

ZAM'S AIRSPEEDER

Manufacturer: Desler Gizh Outworld Mobility Corp.
Make: *Koro-2* all-environment exodrive airspeeder
Dimensions: 6.6 m (21.7 ft); width 2.1 m (7 ft); depth 0.9 m (3 ft)
Max. speed: 800 kph (496 mph)

Cargo Capacity: 80 kg (176 lbs) or 0.04 m³ (1.4 ft³) in cabin and storage bins
Consumables: approx. five years' gas for irradiation system; two weeks' cabin air supply
Hyperdrive: Nubian 288 cores; S-6 generators (class 0.7; range 80,000 light years fully fuelled)
Passengers: 1 (excluding pilot)
Armament: none

ANAKIN'S AIRSPEEDER

Manufacturer: mechanics at Senator Greyshade's private vehicle workshop
Make: unique, custom-built luxury airspeeder hotrod
Dimensions: length 6.23 m (20.4 ft); width 2.66 m (8.7 ft); depth (excluding antennas) 1.4 m (4.6 ft)
Mass: 1,600 kg (3,520 lbs)
Engine power: 30 megawatts
Max. airspeed: 720 kph (450 mph)
Max. acceleration: 70G (approx. engine limit)
Passengers: 1 (excluding pilot)
Armament: none

JEDI STARFIGHTER

Manufacturer: Kuat Systems Engineering, subsidiary of Kuat Drive Yards

Make: Delta-7 *Aethersprite* light interceptor

Dimensions: length 8 m (26 ft); width 3.92 m (12.8 ft); depth 1.44 m (4.7 ft)

Max. speed (in standard atmosphere): 12,000 kph (7,400 mph)

Max. acceleration (linear, in open space): 5,000G

Cargo capacity (in cockpit): 60 kg (132 lbs) or 0.03 m³ (1.06 ft³)

Consumables: five hours' fuel and air in normal sublight operation (air supply prolonged if pilot uses Jedi hibernation trance)

Crew: 1 pilot and 1 modified, integrated astromech droid

Armament: 2 dual laser cannons (1 kiloton per shot max.)

JANGO FETT'S SLAVE I

Manufacturer: Kuat Systems Engineering

Make: *Firespray*-class patrol and attack ship

Dimensions: length 21.5 m (70.5 ft); wingspan 21.3 m (70 ft); depth (excluding guns) 7.8 m (25.6 ft)

Max. speed (in standard atmosphere): 1,000 kph (620 mph)

Max. acceleration (linear, in open space): 2,500G

Hyperdrive: class 1.0

Crew: 1 pilot; up to 2 co-pilots/navigator/gunners

Passengers: 2 seated (immobilized captives are stored in lockers)

Armament: 2 blaster cannons (600 gigajoules per shot); 2 laser cannons (8x10¹² joules per shot); missile-launcher (8x10¹⁷ joules per shot); minelayer (5x10¹⁹ joules per shot); other unknown weapons

OWEN LARS'S SWOOP BIKE

Manufacturer: Mobquet

Make: Zephyr-G

Dimensions: length 3.68 m (12 ft); width 0.66 m (2 ft); depth 0.72 m (2.4 ft)

Max. airspeed: 350 kph (217 mph)

Max. acceleration: 2G (no inertial compensator; limited only by rider's grip and stamina)

Cargo capacity: 50 kg (110 lbs) per pannier; 200 kg (440 lbs) lifting capacity including rider

Consumables: approx. 3,000 km (1,860 miles) worth of fuel

Crew: 1 (and 1 passenger, in discomfort)

Armament: none

PADMÉ'S STARSHIP

Manufacturer: Theed Palace Space Vessel Engineering Corps

Make: Customised H-type Nubian yacht

Propulsion: 2 Nubian Sossen-3 ion drives

Dimensions: length 47.9 m (157 ft); width 8.1 m (26.7 ft); depth 7.1 m (23.3ft)

Max. acceleration (linear, in open space): 2,800G

Max. speed (in standard atmosphere): 8,000 kph

Power: main reactor peak 7x10¹² mw; peak shielding 2x10¹² mw

Hyperdrive: Nubian 150 core and S-5 generator (class 0.9; range 20,000 light years fully fuelled)

Crew: 1 pilot; 1 co-pilot; 2 optional (navigator/comscan plus shield operator); 2 astromech droids

Passengers: 1 prestige cabin

Armament: none

TRADE FEDERATION CORE SHIP

Manufacturer: Hoersch-Kessel Drive Inc. (basic Core Ship); Baktoid Combat Automata (droid-army control core)

Model: Lucrehulk-class modular control core (LH-1740)

Dimensions: diameter 696 m (2285 ft); depth (when landed, minus transmission mast) 914 m (3,000 ft)

Max. acceleration (linear, in open space): 300G

Power: reactor peak 3x10²⁴ watts; peak shield capacity 6x10²³ watts

Cargo capacity: approx. 66 million m³ (2.3 billion ft³)

Consumables: 3 years' supplies

Crew: 60 Trade Federation supervisors; 3,000 Droid Crew; 200,000 Maintenance Droids

Passengers: stateroom capacity for 60,000 trade representatives

Armament: 280 point-defense light laser cannons (8 kilotons per shot max.)

GEONOSIAN FIGHTER

Manufacturer: Huppla Pasa Tisc Shipwrights Collective

Make: Nantex-class territorial defense starfighter

Dimensions (excluding cockpit bubble): length 9.8 m (32 ft); width 1.9 m (6.2 ft); depth 2.2 m (7.2 ft)

Max. speed (in standard atmosphere): 20,000 kph (12,400 mph)

Max. acceleration (linear, in open space): 4,500G

Hyperdrive: none

Crew: 1 pilot (bonded to specific fighter)

Armament: 1 laser cannon turret (1×10^{13} joules per shot); 100 independently aiming narrow-beam tractor/repulsor projectors

AT-TE

Manufacturer: Rothana Heavy Engineering (local subsidiary of Kuat Drive Yards)

Make: AT-TE (All Terrain Tactical Enforcer) assault walker

Dimensions: (hull only) length 13.2 m (43.3 ft); width 5.7 m (18.7 ft); (hull and legs) height 5.7 m (18.7 ft)

Max. landspeed: 60 kph (37.2 mph)

Consumables: fuel for 500 km (310 miles) walking; three standard weeks' air and rations

Crew: 1 pilot; 1 spotter; 4 gunner/support crew; 1 turret gunner outside

Passengers: 20 clone troopers; 1 IM-6 Battlefield Medical Droid (stowed in emergency locker)

Armament: 6 anti-personnel laser cannon turrets (4 front; 2 back; 5×10^9 joules per shot max.); 1 heavy projectile cannon (variable yield)

REPUBLIC ASSAULT SHIP

Manufacturer: Rothana Heavy Engineering (subsidiary of KDY)

Make: *Acclamator*-class trans-galactic military transport ship

Dimensions: length 752 m (2,466 ft); width 460 m (1,509 ft); depth (with landing gear); 200 m (656 ft); depth (in flight) 183 m (600 ft)

Max. acceleration (linear, in open space): 3,500G

Power: main reactor peak 2×10^{23} watts; peak shielding 7×10^{22} watts

Hyperdrive: class 0.6; range 250,000 light-years fully fuelled

Cargo capacity: 320 speeder bikes; 80 infantry and cargo gunships; 48 armored walkers; 36 heavy self-propelled artillery pieces; 200,000 m³ (7,060,000 ft³) cargo space in addition to hangar space and consumables

Crew: 700

Passengers: 16,000 clone troops and support personnel

Armament: 12 quad turbolaser turrets (200 gigatons per shot); 24 laser cannons (6 megatons per shot); 4 missile/torpedo launch tubes

REPUBLIC GUNSHIP

Manufacturer: Rothana Heavy Engineering (local subsidiary of KDY)

Make: LAAT/i (Low-Altitude Assault Transport/infantry) repulsorlift gunship

Dimensions: length (clearance with guns) 17.4 m (57 ft); wingspan 17 m (55.7 ft); depth 6.1 m (20 ft)

Max. airspeed: 620 kph (384 mph)

Cargo capacity: 4 military speeder bikes; approx. 17 m³ (600 ft³) in main hold (if troops absent)

Consumables: 8 hours' flying fuel (approx.)

Crew: 1 pilot; 1 co-pilot/gunner; 2 auxiliary turret gunners

Passengers: 30 clone troopers approx.; 1 IM-6 Battlefield Medical Droid (stowed in emergency locker)

Armament: 3 anti-personnel turrets (2 front; 1 back; 5×10^9 joules per shot); 2 mass-driver missile launchers (variable payload); 4 composite-beam, pinpoint laser turrets (2 manned; 2 remote; 3×10^{11} joules per shot); 8 light air-to-air rockets (6×10^{11} joules per shot)

DOOKU'S SOLAR SAILER

Manufacturer: Huppla Pasa Tisc Shipwrights Collective

Make: *Punworcca 116*-class interstellar sloop

Dimensions: (with sail undeployed) length 16.8m (55 ft); width 4.6m (15 ft); depth 4.8m (15.7 ft)

Max. acceleration: sail approx. 1,000G; thrusters 30G

Max. airspeed: 1,600 kph (992 mph)

Crew: 1 droid pilot; optional living co-pilot

Passengers: 1 in cabin; standing room for 10

Hyperdrive : class 1.5

Armament: 84 narrow tractor/repulsor beams

STAR DESTROYER – VENATOR CLASS

Manufacturer: Kuat Drive Yards

Make: *Venator*-class Star Destroyer

Dimensions: length 1,137 m (3,729 ft); wingspan 548 m (1,797 ft); height (in flight) 268 m (87.9 ft)

Max. acceleration (linear, in open space): 3,000G

Hyperdrive: class 1.0; 60,000 light year effective range

Crew: 7,400

Armament: 8 heavy turbolaser turrets; 2 medium dual turbolaser cannons; 52 point-defense laser cannons; 4 proton torpedo tubes; 6 tractor beam projectors

Complement: 192 V-wing fighters; 192 Eta-2 *Actis* Interceptors; 36 ARC-170 fighters; 24 military walkers; 40 LAAT/i (Low Altitude Assault Transport/infantry) gunships; miscellaneous shuttles

TRI-FIGHTER

Manufacturer: Colla Designs and Phlac-Arphocc Automata Industries

Make: space superiority starfighter

Dimensions: length 5.4 m (17.7 ft); wing diameter 1.96 m (6.4 ft); width 3.45 m (11.3 ft)

Max. acceleration (linear, in open space): 3,600G

Max. airspeed (in standard atmosphere): 37,000 kph (22,990 mph)

Hyperdrive: none

Crew: integrated droid brain

Armament: 1 medium laser cannon; 3 light laser cannons; 2–6 buzz-droid missiles

ARC-170 STARFIGHTER

Manufacturer: Incom/Subpro

Make: ARC-170 (Aggressive ReConnaissance starfighter)

Dimensions: length 14.5 m (47.5 ft); wingspan 22.6 m (75 ft); height 4.78 m (15.7 ft)

Max. acceleration (linear, in open space): 2,600G

Max. airspeed (in standard atmosphere): 44,000 kph (27,341 mph)

Hyperdrive: class 1.5; 5,000 light-year range

Consumables: 5 days' air

Crew: 3 (pilot/copilot/gunner); 1 astromech droid

Armament: 2 medium laser cannons; 2 aft laser cannons; 6 proton torpedoes

V-WING STARFIGHTER

Manufacturer: Kuat Systems Engineering

Make: Alpha-3 Nimbus "V-wing" starfighter

Dimensions: length 7.9 m (26 ft); width 3.8 m (12.5 ft); height with open wings 5.84 m (19 ft)

Max. acceleration (linear, in open space): 4,800G

Max. airspeed (in standard atmosphere): 52,000 kph (32,312 mph)

Hyperdrive: none

Consumables: 15 hours' air

Crew: 1 pilot and 1 astromech droid

Armament: 2 twin laser cannons

JEDI INTERCEPTOR

Manufacturer: Kuat Systems Engineering, subsidiary of Kuat Drive Yards (fighter); TransGalMeg Industries Inc. (hyperdrive ring)

Make: Eta-2 *Actis* Interceptor; Syliure-45 hyperdrive module

Dimensions: length 5.47 m (18 ft); width 4.3 m (14.1 ft); height with open wings 2.5 m (8.2 ft)

Max. acceleration (linear, in open space): 5,200G

Max. speed (in standard atmosphere): 15,000 kph (9,321 mph)

Crew: 1 pilot and 1 astromech droid

Shields: none

Armament: 2 dual laser cannons; 2 secondary ion cannons

DROID GUNSHIP

Manufacturer: Baktoid Fleet Ordnance

Make: HMP (Heavy Missile Platform) droid gunship

Function: Ground assault fighter

Dimensions (excluding guns): length 12.3 m (40.5 ft); width 11 m (36.2 ft); height 3.1 m (10.2 ft)

Max. acceleration (linear, in open space): 100G

Max. airspeed (in standard atmosphere): 14,200 kph (8,824 mph)

Crew: Integrated droid brain

Armament (standard configuration): 2 laser cannon turrets; 1 medium laser cannon; 2 light laser cannons; 14 missiles

DATA FILES CONTINUED

JUGGERNAUT

Manufacturer: Kuat Drive Yards

Make: HAVw A6 Juggernaut

Dimensions: length 49.4 m (162 ft); width 19.6 m (64.2 ft); height 30.4 m (99.6 ft)

Max. landspeed: 160 kph (99 mph)

Crew: 12 (excluding gunners)

Passengers: 50–300 depending on internal configuration

Consumables: 20 days' provisions; fuel for 30,000 km (18,641 miles)

Armament: 1 heavy laser cannon turret; 1 rapid repeating laser cannon; 2 medium antipersonnel laser cannons; 2 twin blaster cannons; 2 rocket/grenade launchers—variable yield, 30 km (19.6 miles) range

INVISIBLE HAND

Manufacturer: Free Dac Volunteers, Pammant Docks

Make: Modified Providence-class carrier/destroyer

Dimensions: length 1,088 m (3,570 ft); width 198 m (650 ft); height 347 m (1,139 ft)

Propulsion: 4 Nubian Creveld-4 radial ion drives

Max. acceleration (linear, in open space): 2,500G

Max. speed (in standard atmosphere): 2,000 kph (1,240 mph)

Hyperdrive: class 1.5; 40,000 light-year effective range

Crew: 600; up to 1.5 million deactivated battle droids

Armament: 14 quad turbolaser turrets; 34 dual laser cannons; 2 ion cannons; 12 point-defense ion cannons; 102 proton torpedo tubes

Complement: 120 droid tri-fighters; 120 droid Vulture fighters; 160 MTTs (Multi-Troop Transport); 280 assorted droid armored vehicles

AT-RT

Manufacturer: Kuat Drive Yards

Product line: All Terrain Series

Height: 3.7 m (12.1 ft)

Crew: 1 pilot

Max. speed: 75 kph (46.6 mph)

Armament: 1 laser cannon

Cargo capacity: 20kg

Consumables: 1 day

BANKING CLAN FRIGATE

Manufacturer: Hoersch-Kessel Drive Inc. and Gwori Revolutionary Industries

Make: Munificent-class star frigate

Dimensions: length 825 m (2,706 ft); width 426 m (1,397 ft); height 243 m (797 ft)

Max. acceleration (linear, in open space): 2,300G

Hyperdrive: class 1.0; 150,000 light-year effective range

Crew: 200; up to 150,000 deactivated battle droids

Weapons: 2 heavy turbolaser cannons; 2 long-range ion cannons; 26 twin turbolaser cannons; 20 light turbolaser turrets; 38 point-defense laser cannons

COMMERCE GUILD DESTROYER

Manufacturer: Hoersch-Kessel Drive Inc. and Free Dac Volunteers Engineering Corps

Make: Recusant-class light destroyer

Dimensions: length 1,187 m (3,893 ft); width 157 m (515 ft); height 163 m (535 ft)

Max. acceleration (linear, in open space): 2,800G

Hyperdrive: class 2.0; 30,000 light-year effective range

Crew: 300; up to 40,000 deactivated battle droids

Armament: 1 prow heavy turbolaser cannon; 4 heavy turbolaser cannons; 6 heavy turbolaser turrets; 5 turbolaser cannons; 30 dual laser cannons; 12 dual light laser cannons 60 point-defense laser cannons

UTAPAUN STARFIGHTER

Manufacturer: Buuper Torsckil Abbey Devices

Make: Porax-38 (P-38) starfighter

Dimensions: length 12.7 m (41.7 ft); width 12.88 m (42.3 ft); height 2.71 m (8.9 ft)

Max. acceleration (linear, in open space): 3,300G

Max. airspeed (in standard atmosphere): 61,000 kph (37, 905 mph)

Hyperdrive: class 2; 3,000 light-year effective range

Consumables: 20 days' air, fuel, and food

Crew: 1

Armament: 2 laser cannons

MANKVIM-814 LIGHT INTERCEPTOR

Manufacturer: Feethan Ottraw Scalable Assemblies

Make: Mankvim-814 light interceptor

Dimensions: length 10.7 m (35 ft); width 6.46 m (21.2 ft); height 3.45 m (11.3 ft)

Max. acceleration (linear, in open space): 3,400G

Max. airspeed (in standard atmosphere): 62,000 kph (37,905 mph)

Hyperdrive: none

Consumables: 2 hours' fuel

Crew: 1

Armament: 2 laser cannons

GRIEVOUS'S WHEEL BIKE

Manufacturer: Z-Gomot Ternbuell Guppat Corp., Zug system

Make: Tsmeu-6 personal wheel bike

Dimensions: wheel diameter 2.5 m (8.3 ft); length (including double laser cannon, excluding legs) 3.5 m (11.5 ft); height (including legs) 3.9 m (12.8 ft)

Crew: 1

Max. landspeed: 330 kph (205 mph) rolling; 10 kph (6 mph) on legs

Consumables: fuel for 500 km (311 miles) travel

Armament: 1 double laser cannon

WOOKIEE CATAMARAN

Manufacturer: Appazanna Engineering Works

Make: *Oevvaor* jet catamaran

Dimensions: length 15.1 m (46.2 ft); width 10.2 m (33.5 ft); height 4.3 m (14.1 ft)

Max. waterspeed: 370 kph (230 mph)

Crew: 2

Passengers: 2

Consumables: 2 days' rations

Armament: none

PALPATINE'S SHUTTLE

Manufacturer: Cygnus Spaceworks

Make: *Theta*-class T-2c Personnel Transport

Dimensions: length (excluding guns) 18.5 m (60.7 ft); width 29.3 m (96.1 ft); height 18.5 m (60.7 ft)

Max. acceleration (linear, in open space): 1,800G

Max. airspeed (in standard atmosphere): 2,000 kph (1,240 mph)

Hyperdrive: class 1; 8,000 light-year range

Consumables: 60 days fuel and air

Crew: 1–5

Armament: 2 quad laser cannons; 1 aft laser cannon

KASHYYYK POD

Manufacturer: Uurbahhahvoovv Joiners & Artisans

Make: homemade evacuation pod

Dimensions: diameter 2.3 m (7.5 ft); height 3.4 m (11.1 ft)

Max. acceleration (linear, in open space): 140G

Max. airspeed (during descent): over 70,000 kph (43,497 mph)

Hyperdrive: none

Passengers: 1

Consumables: 1 week's food and air

DAGOBAH POD

Manufacturer: His Grace the Duke Gadal-Herm's Safety Inspectorate

Dimensions: diameter 3.5 m (11.5 ft); length (legs retracted) 4 m (13.1 ft)

Make: E3-standard starship lifeboat

Max. acceleration (linear, in open space): 300G

Max. airspeed (during descent): over 40,000 kph (24,856 mph)

Hyperdrive: none

Passengers: 3

Consumables: 4 weeks' food and air

DATA FILES CONTINUED

SANDCRAWLER

Manufacturer: Corellia Mining Corporation

Make: Corellia Mining Corporation digger/crawler

Length: 36.8 m (120.7 ft)

Height: 20 m (65.6 ft)

Crew: approximately 50 (members of single Jawa clan)

Engines: Girodyne Ka/La steampowered nuclear fusion engine

Max. speed: 30 kph (18.6 mph)

Cargo capacity: approximately 50 metric tons (110,231 lbs), in addition to storage for 1,500 droids

Consumables: 2 months' fuel and food

Armament: None

TANTIVE IV

Manufacturer: Corellian Engineering Corporation

Make: CR90 Corellian Corvette ("Blockade Runner")

Length: original; 150 m (492.1 ft) after refit; 125 m (410.1 ft)

Crew: 85 (46 crew, 39 diplomatic/consular staff)

Engines: 11 Girodyne Ter58 ion turbine engines

Hyperdrive: class 2

Armament: 6 Taim & Bak H9 turbolasers (2 dual, 4 single)

LUKE'S LANDSPEEDER

Manufacturer: SoroSuub Corporation

Length: 3.4 m (11.2 ft)

Crew: 1 pilot

Passengers: 1

Max. speed: 250 kph (155.3 mph)

Max. altitude: 1 m (3.3 ft)

Armament: None

STAR DESTROYER

Manufacturer: Kuat Drive Yards

Make: *Imperial-I* Star Destroyer

Length: 1,600 m (5,249.3 ft)

Crew: (standard complement): 9,235 officers, 27,850 enlisted, 9,700 stormtroopers

Engines: SFS I-a2b solar ionization reactor powering Cygnus Spaceworks Gemon-4 ion engines

Hyperdrive: class 2

Complement: 48 TIE/ln fighters, 12 TIE bombers, 12 TIE boarding craft, 12 landing craft, 20 AT-AT walkers, 30 AT-ST walkers, 8 *Lambda*-class Imperial shuttles, 15 stormtrooper transports, 5 assault gunboats

Armament: 60 Taim & Bak XX-9 heavy turbolaser batteries, 60 Borstel NK- 7 ion cannons, 10 Phylon Q7 tractor beam projectors

MILLENNIUM FALCON

Manufacturer: Corellian Engineering Corporation

Make: Corellian YT-1300 transport (modified)

Length: 26.7 m (87.6 ft)

Crew: 2 (minimum)

Passengers: 6

Cargo: 100 metric tons (220,462 lbs)

Engines: Quadex power core, powering Isu-Sim SSP05 hyperdrive generator (heavily modified); 2 Girodyne SRB42 sublight engines (heavily modified)

Hyperdrive: class 0.5

Armament: 2 CEC AG-2G quad laser cannons, 2 Arakyd ST2 concussion missile tubes, 1 BlasTech Ax-108 "Ground Buzzer" blaster cannon

DEATH STAR

Manufacturer: Imperial Department of Military Research/Sienar Fleet Systems (construction overseen by Wilhuff Tarkin)

Designer: Initial conceptual design by Raith Sienar, stolen by Tarkin. Further developed by Geonosian Hive engineers, with final design by Bevel Lemelisk

Make: Mk.1 deep-space mobile battle station

Dimensions: 160 km (99.4 miles) diameter; interior comprising 84 levels, each 1,428 m (4,685 ft) in height, each level divided into 357 sublevels, 4 m (13.1 ft) in height

Crew: 342,953 (285,675 operational staff, 57,278 gunners)

Passengers: 843,342

Hyperdrive: class 4

Engines: SFS-CR27200 hypermatter reactor powering 123 Isu-Sim SSP06 hyperdrive generators; 2 Sepma 30-5 sublight engines

Armament: 1 superlaser—range 47,060,000 km (29,241,719 miles), 5,000 Taim & Bak D6 turbolaser batteries, 5,000 Taim & Bak XX-9 heavy turbolasers, 2,500 SFS L-s 4.9 laser cannons, 2,500 Borstel MS-1 ion cannons, 768 Phylon tractorbeam emplacements, 11,000 combat vehicles

T-65 X-WING

Manufacturer: Incom Corporation

Designer: Vors Voorhorian (lead designer)

Make: Incom T-65C-A2 X-wing starfighter

Length: 12.5 m (41 ft)

Crew: 1 pilot and 1 astromech droid

Engines: Incom GBk-585 hyperdrive; 4 Incom 4L4 fusial thrust engines

Hyperdrive: class 1

Armament: 4 Taim & Bak KX9 laser cannons, 2 Krupx MG7 proton torpedo launchers

BTL A-4 Y-WING

Manufacturer: Koensayr

Make: BTL-A4 Y-wing starfighter

Length: 16 m (52.5 ft)

Crew: 1 or 2, and 1 astromech droid

Engines: Koensayr R300-H hyperdrive; 2 Koensayr R200 ion fission engines

Hyperdrive: class 1

Armament: 2 Taim & Bak KX5 laser cannons, 2 Arakyd Flex Tube proton torpedo launchers (4 torpedoes per launcher), 2 ArMek SW-4 light ion cannons

AT-AT

Manufacturer: Kuat Drive Yards

Designer: Imperial Department of Military Research

Make: Imperial All Terrain Armored Transport

Length: 20.6 m (67.6 ft)

Height: 15.5 m (50.9 ft)

Crew: 3

Passengers: 40

Cargo: 5 speeder bikes

Engines: 2 KDYFW62 compact fusion drive systems

Max. speed: 60 kph (37.3 mph)

Armament: 2 Taim & Bak MS-1 heavy laser cannons, 2 Taim & Bak FF-4 medium repeating blasters

SNOWSPEEDER

Manufacturer: Incom Corporation

Make: Incom T-47 airspeeder (modified)

Length: 5.3 m (17.4 ft)

Crew: 2

Engines: 2 Karydee KD49 repulsorlift drive units; 2 Incom 5i.2 high-powered ion drive afterburners

Max. speed: 1,100 kph (683.5 mph)

Flight ceiling: 175 km (108.7 miles)

Armament: 1 CEC Ap/11 double laser cannon, Ubrikkian Mo/Dk power harpoon and tow cable

AT-ST

Manufacturer: Kuat Drive Yards

Designer: Imperial Department of Military Research

Make: Imperial All Terrain Scout Transport

Height: 8.6 m (28.2 ft)

Crew: 2

Cargo: 200 kg (440.9 lbs)

Engines: PowaTek AH-50 disposable high-intensity power cells

Max. speed: 90 kph (55.6 mph)

Armament: 1 Taim & Bak MS-4 twin blaster cannon, 1 E-web twin light blaster cannon, Dymek DW-3 concussion grenade launcher

DATA FILES CONTINUED

TIE FIGHTER

Manufacturer: Sienar Fleet Systems (for all TIE variants)

Make: TIE/ln space superiority fighter

Length: 6.3 m (20.7 ft)

Crew: 1 pilot

Engines: SFS I-a2b solar ionization reactor powering SFS P-s4 twin ion engines

Hyperdrive: none

Consumables: 2 days' air and food

Armament: 2 Sienar Fleet Systems L-s1 laser cannons

TIE BOMBER

Make: TIE bomber

Length: 7.8 m (25.6 ft)

Crew: 1 pilot

Engines: SFS I-a2b solar ionization reactor powering SFS P-s4 twin ion engines

Hyperdrive: none

Consumables: 2 days' air and food

Armament: 2 SFS L-s1 laser cannons, SFS-M-s3 concussion missiles; ArmaTek SJ-62/68 orbital mines, ArmaTek VL-61/79 proton bombs

TIE ADVANCED X1

Make: TIE Advanced x1 starfighter

Length: 9.2 m (30.2 ft)

Crew: 1 pilot

Engines: SFS I-S3a solar ionization reactor powering SFS P-s5.6 twin ion engines

Hyperdrive: class 4

Consumables: 5 days' air and food

Armament: 2 Sienar Fleet Systems L-s9.3 TIE laser cannons

TIE INTERCEPTOR

Make: TIE interceptor

Length: 9.6 m (31.5 ft)

Crew: 1 pilot

Engines: SFS I-a3a solar ionization reactor powering SFS P-s5.6 twin ion engines

Hyperdrive: none

Consumables: 2 days' air and food

Armament: 4 Sienar Fleet Systems L-s9.3 laser cannons

SLAVE I

Manufacturer: Kuat Systems Engineering

Make: *Firespray*-class patrol craft

Length: 21.5 m (70.5 ft)

Crew: 1

Passengers: 6 (prisoners)

Engines: 4 Kuat X-F-16 generators powering Kuat Engineering Systems F-31 ion engines

Hyperdrive: class 1

Armament: Borstel GN-40 twin rotating blaster cannons, 2 Dymek HM-8 concussion missile tube launchers, Brugiss C/ln ion cannon, Phylon F1 tractor beam projector, 2 Arakyd AA/SL proton torpedo launchers (3 torpedoes per launcher)

NEBULON-B FRIGATE (MEDICAL CONVERSION)

Manufacturer: Kuat Drive Yards

Length: 300 m (984.2 ft)

Crew: 850 (77 officers, 773 enlisted)

Passengers: 80 (medical personnel), and up to 745 patients

Engines: Kuat Galaxy-15 ion engines

Hyperdrive: Triple Taim, class 2

Armament: 6 Taim & Bak XI 7 turbolasers, 8 Borstel RH8 laser cannons, 2 Phylon-Q7 tractor beam projectors

HOME ONE

Manufacturer: Mon Calamari Shipyards

Length: 1,300 m (4265.1 ft)

Crew: 5,500

Passengers: 1,200 troops

Engines: M8.0-StarDrive engines

Hyperdrive: TriLuna 400MGS

Complement: 120 starfighters (mixture of A-wings, B-wings, X-wings, and Y-wings)

Armament: 36 heavy turbolasers, 36 heavy ion cannons

JABBA'S SAIL BARGE

Manufacturer: Ubrikkian Custom Vehicle Division

Make: Ubrikkian luxury sail barge *Khetanna*

Length: 30 m (98.4 ft)

Crew: 26

Passengers: 500

Engines: 3 Karydee KD57 3-chamber repulsorlift engines

Max. speed: 100 kph (62.1 mph)

Armament: 1 CEC Me/7double laser cannon; 20 CEC Gi/9 antipersonnel laser cannons

RZ-1 A-WING

Manufacturer: Various Alliance-linked organizations

Designer: General Jan Dodonna, with Walex Blissex

Make: RZ-1 A-Wing starfighter

Length: 9.6 m (31.5 ft)

Crew: 1 pilot

Engines: 2 Novaldex J-77 "Event Horizon" engines

Hyperdrive: class 1

Armament: 2 Borstel RG9 laser cannons, 2 Dymek HM-6 concussion missile launchers (6 missiles per launcher)

B-WING STARFIGHTER

Manufacturer: Slayn & Korpil

Designer: Commander Ackbar (with assistance of Verpine engineers)

Make: B-wing heavy assault starfighter

Length: 16.9 m (55.4 ft)

Crew: 1 pilot

Engines: 1 Quadex Kyromaster engine with 4 thrust nozzles (or alternatively 4 Slayn & Korpil JZ-5 fusial thrust engines)

Hyperdrive: class 2

Armament (standard configuration) : 3 ArMek SW-7a ion cannons; 1 Gyrhil R-9X heavy laser cannon; Gyrhil 72 twin auto-blasters; 2 Krupx MG9 proton torpedo launchers

IMPERIAL SHUTTLE

Manufacturer: Sienar Fleet Systems

Make: *Lambda*-class Shuttle

Length: 20 m (65.6 ft)

Crew: 2–6

Passengers: 10–20 (or 80 metric tons [176,370 lbs] of cargo)

Engines: SFS S/ig-37 hyperdrive engine; 2 SFS-204 sublight ion engines

Hyperdrive: class 1

Armament (shuttle Tydirium configuration): 2 Taim & Bak KX5 double blaster cannons (forward-mounted), 1 ArMek R-Z0 retractable double blaster cannon (rear-mounted), 2 Taim & Bak GA-60s double laser cannons

SCOUT SPEEDER BIKE

Manufacturer: Aratech Repulsor Company

Make: 74-Z speeder bike

Length: 3 m (9.8 ft)

Crew: 1 pilot

Max. airspeed: 500 kph (310.6 mph)

Armament: 1 light blaster cannon

Cargo capacity: 3 kilograms

Consumables: 1 day

GLOSSARY

ASTROMECH (DROID)

Multipurpose utility droid, designed primarily for use in spacecraft. Many starfighters incorporate an integral astromech droid to assist with astronavigation.

BLASTER CANNON

Limited-range, heavy artillery weapon fitted to starships for defensive use. Blasters utilize high-energy blaster gas to produce a visible beam of intense energy, which can cause tremendous damage to structures and organic tissue. Although their destructive power is considerable, blaster cannons are not as powerful as laser cannons.

CAPITAL SHIP

A large military starship designed for deep-space warfare, such as an Imperial Star Destroyer or Mon Calamari Star Cruiser. With crews numbering in the hundreds or even thousands, capital ships have numerous heavy weapons and shields. They often carry shuttles, starfighters, and other craft in their huge hangar bays.

**Assault Ship –
Acclamator Class**

CLOAKING DEVICE

Used to render a starship invisible to electronic detection systems, a cloaking device disrupts the electronic signature normally emitted by a craft's various systems and sensors.

CONCUSSION MISSILE

A projectile that travels at sublight speed and causes destructive shockwaves on impact with its target. Concussion missiles are capable of penetrating the armor of a capital ship.

DROID

Generic term for any form of mobile robotic system that has at least some of the capabilities of locomotion, manipulation, logic, self-aware intelligence, communication, and sensory reception. Droids are usually fashioned in the likeness of their creators, or else are designed for functionality. Programmed with varying degrees of artificial intelligence and powered by internal rechargeable cells, droids are the workhorses of the galaxy. They are employed for an incredibly broad range of tasks, from field and manufacturing labor to use as soldiers, assassins, mechanics, diplomatic aides, and doctors. Many cultures treat droids as slaves or second-class beings. There are over fifty billion droids in current service in the galaxy.

**Trade Federation
Droid Starfighter**

ESCAPE POD

A space capsule used by passengers and crew to abandon starships in emergencies. Once launched, an escape pod uses its sensor systems to collect data on nearby planets, then utilizes its simple drive system to enter the atmosphere of the nearest hospitable world and achieve a safe landing. Pods have a limited fuel supply, but are equipped with up to two weeks' supplies to aid passenger survival.

HEAT SINKS & RADIATORS

Devices designed to draw away heat generated by spacecraft or vehicle systems and dissipate it into the surrounding environment. Removing this "waste heat" keeps the system's components within their normal operating temperature, preventing malfunctions and breakdowns.

**Jedi Interceptor with
Hyperdrive Booster**

HYPERDRIVE

The "faster-than-light" drive that allows a starship to enter the alternate dimension known as hyperspace, where the normal laws of space and time no longer apply. By traveling through hyperspace, vehicles can cross vast distances of space in an instant.

HYPERDRIVE CLASS

Hyperdrives are rated by "classes": the lower the class, the faster the hyperdrive. Most civilian ships use relatively slow hyperdrives rated at Class Three or higher. Government, diplomatic, and military vessels have Class Two or Class One hyperdrives, while some experimental or "rogue" craft, such as the *Millennium Falcon*, use even faster classes.

INERTIAL COMPENSATOR

A device that generates a type of artificial gravity, which helps to neutralize the effects of accelerating to high speeds aboard medium- and larger-sized spacecraft, such as the *Millennium Falcon*.

ION CANNON

A weapon that fires powerful bolts of ionized energy designed to overload a target's systems or fuse its mechanical components. It is used to disable an opposing starship without causing lasting damage.

**Rebel Alliance
Snowspeeder**

ION DRIVE

An extremely common form of sublight drive, employed to transport starships into orbit from planetary surfaces and through local space. Ion engines produce thrust by projecting a stream of charged particles. There are many ion engine configurations, but one of the most successful designs is the twin ion engine utilized in the TIE family of starfighters.

Imperial TIE Fighter

LASER CANNON

The dominant weapon in the galaxy, found on both military and civilian spacecraft and vehicles. Laser cannons are a more powerful form of blaster, firing bolts of concentrated energy. They can range from low-grade models—which are only slightly more powerful than blaster rifles—to military versions capable of destroying starfighters with a single blast.

PROTON BOMB

A form of particle weapon that can be dropped onto spacecraft or planetary-surface installations. The bomb creates a cloud of high-velocity protons that can penetrate defensive shields. There are several types of proton bombs in the Imperial arsenal

PROTON TORPEDO

A high-speed projectile weapon that destroys its targets by releasing a wave of high-energy proton particles on impact. It can bypass standard deflector shielding but can be stopped by particle shielding.

Proton Torpedo

QUAD LASER

Laser weapon consisting of four linked laser cannons which fire alternately in pairs. Quad lasers are very powerful in comparison to many ship-mounted weapons, but more affordable than turbolasers. They are commonly used on small- to medium-sized starships.

REPULSORLIFT

Antigravity technology used by planet-based vehicles. Repulsorlifts create an antigravity field which repels a planet's gravity, providing lift that enables a craft to hover over the surface or fly in the atmosphere. Most starships also use repulsorlift technology for planetary landings and atmospheric flight.

Battle Droid & STAP (Single Trooper Aerial Platform)

SENSOR ARRAY

A suite of information-gathering instruments fitted to a spacecraft or vehicle. A sensor array is composed of a number of different scanners and other detection instruments that provide data on the environment surrounding the craft.

SHIELDS

Also known as deflector shields, these protective energy fields absorb laser blasts and deflect physical projectiles. Almost all spacecraft and some vehicles are protected by shields. The strength, radius, and endurance depend upon the available power supply. There are two main types of shields: ray shields, which absorb radiation and raw energy; and particle shields, which repel solid objects, from proton particles to concussion and proton weapons.

Republic ISP (Infantry Support Platform)

SPEEDER

Generic term for a ground vehicle that uses repulsorlift technology to hover and fly above a planet's surface. Variations for different environments include landspeeders, airspeeders, and snowspeeders.

SPEEDER BIKES & SWOOPS

Personal ground-transport vehicles that use the same repulsorlift technology as speeders to travel across a planet's surface. Designed to carry one or two passengers, speeder bikes are in use throughout the galaxy for both civilian and military transportation. Swoops are high-powered versions of the speeder bike that are faster and more difficult to control. Swoop racing is a common sporting event throughout the galaxy.

Sith Speeder Bike

STARFIGHTER

A small, fast, maneuverable, and heavily armed starship used in direct confrontations between opposing forces. Most space battles are fought between squadrons of starfighters.

Techno Union Starfighter

SUBLIGHT DRIVE

A form of propulsion used for non-hyperspace travel. Spacecraft use sublight drives to lift off from planetary surfaces and travel into orbit. They can also be used to travel into deep space, where a vessel can engage its hyperdrive if necessary. During space battles, all starships engage their sublight drives.

TRACTOR BEAM

Modified force field capable of immobilizing and moving objects in space. Tractor beams can be used by spacecraft and space stations to guide spacecraft into landing bays, move cargo or salvage, or capture enemy vessels for boarding or destruction.

TRANSPORT

A starship used to carry cargo or passengers. The term is usually applied to civilian vessels, but can also refer to a ship that ferries troops and military supplies.

Trade Federation Battleship

TURBOLASER

A high-powered form of laser cannon developed for use on capital ships. Turbolasers require large generators for power and multiperson crews to operate, but can penetrate the shields and armor of opposing capital ships. They are also effective against planetary targets.

Republic Star Destroyer Turbolaser Turret

RICHARD CHASEMORE

W hen Richard (Rich) Chasemore was approached by DK to work on their *Star Wars: Incredible Cross-Sections* books, he had only ever seen one of the films. However, Rich was soon deeply immersed in the worlds of *Star Wars*. He has since gained an in-depth understanding of the intricacies of the *Star Wars* galaxy, and is now a die-hard fan of George Lucas's movie saga. Rich and fellow *Cross-Sections* illustrator, Hans Jenssen, have been collaborating on technical cutaway (cross-section) artworks for more than a decade. Over the years Chasemore has fine-tuned his skills in creating cross-section artworks and developed a particular interest in illustrating cutaways of armored vehicles.

TRAINING AND TEACHING

Rich completed a four-year course in technical illustration in 1992 and went on to work as an illustrator specializing in cutaway technical art. Using both traditional and digital media, he has undertaken a huge variety of publishing and advertising projects. Chasemore also likes to impart his love of drawing to others. He has run an airbrush course in St. Louis, Missouri and has written a number of educational books on digital art.

DRAWING THE TIE BOMBER

During the pencil-drawing process, Rich makes sure that everything that should be depicted inside the craft is included. Chasemore says he "has to be mindful of the exterior shape" while making sure that the design of the internal components works in a realistic way.

Rich's first pencil sketch shows the key elements to be included.

More detail and perspective lines are added.

The final pencil drawing.

Chasemore now begins to ink in the lines.

As the inking progresses, more fine detail is added. By this stage all, the details to be inked-in have been approved by Lucasfilm.

BACK AT THE RANCH

To ensure that each illustration was as accurate as possible, Rich and Hans were given privileged access to the Lucasfilm Archives at Skywalker Ranch, California. They examined original models from Episodes IV to VI and studied how individual vehicle designs were developed. In addition, Rich and Hans had direct discussions with the prequel concept artists and designers about their visions for each vehicle in Episodes I to III.

TIE bomber interior (studio-set shot)

Original Lucasfilm model of TIE bomber

Rich has six of these "curves" for drawing accurate ellipses

A messy paint-palette contrasts with Rich's total control of the painting process

Chasemore has had his airbrush cleaning brush since his college days

A number 1 sable brush is ideal for fine lines

ANNOTATING THE ILLUSTRATION

Rich must work out what to include in the cutaway drawing to ensure continuity with the *Star Wars* movies. Meanwhile, the author works with him and Lucasfilm to decide which parts of the artwork to annotate with technical information. Next, the author develops a draft set of annotations for Lucasfilm approval.

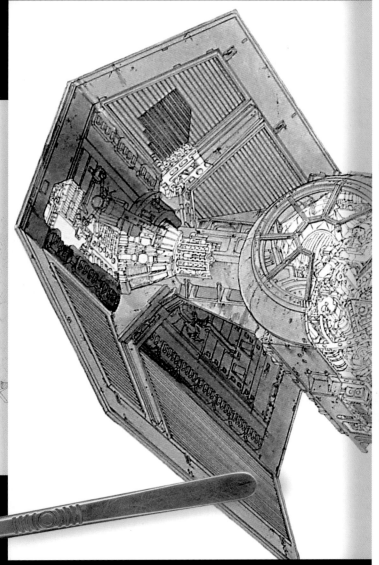

The first "wash" colors the main parts of the craft and indicates the direction of light and shadow.

The TIE bomber artwork is shown above in relation to Rich's number 7 brush, highlighting the size of the artwork and the incredibly detailed work that went into it.

PAINTING THE ARTWORK

According to Rich, "Painting is where the fun really starts." Making sure the direction of the light is right and adding appropriate streaks and blemishes in the "dirtying down" process can "help make the ship jump right out of the page." Colors are often the most difficult part of the process, so Rich constantly has to make careful decisions about which colors to use on different parts of the craft.

With the paint added, the TIE bomber is nearly complete (above, main image). Chasemore uses dry-brush techniques to scrub dirt into the corners and around the base of shapes, to depict the realistic wear and tear a craft would suffer. "I try to think how real-world objects get dirty and reproduce the effects," he says.

Rich uses gouache paints, as they are opaque; this makes them ideal for use in detail work

HANS JENSSEN

The theatrical release of *Star Wars* in 1977 had a huge impact on the young Hans Jenssen. "I was just blown away by the awesome sight of the Star Destroyer flying over my head as I sat in the cinema as a 16-year-old," says the *Star Wars: Incredible Cross-Sections* illustrator. A professional illustrator for more than two decades, Hans combines his artistic skills with his lifelong interest in *Star Wars* to create realistic depictions of the interiors and workings of the saga's spacecraft and vehicles. "From the time I was a kid, I always wanted to know what made machines tick and I loved cutaway art. I especially loved all the *Star Wars* vehicles: my all-time favorite is the AT-AT."

BASIC TRAINING

Hans Jenssen studied graphic design and specialized in technical illustration. "We illustrated boring stuff like plumbing and water pumps. You had to pay your dues...". He decided to specialize in cutaway (cross-section) illustrations, and has worked on a wide range of projects including advertising work for shipping and aerospace companies.

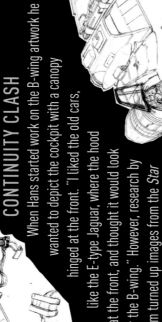

CONTINUITY CLASH

When Hans started work on the B-wing artwork he wanted to depict the cockpit with a canopy hinged at the front. "I liked the old cars, like the E-type Jaguar, where the hood hinged at the front, and thought it would look good for the B-wing." However, research by Lucasfilm turned up images from the *Star Wars* video games showing the canopy hinged at the rear. So the initial drawing (left) had to be modified (right) to maintain continuity.

FINAL PAINTING

To color the artwork Jenssen uses acrylic gouache, ordinary gouache, and watercolor. The acrylic lays down permanent color over large areas. Then Hans can work over it and scrub away areas to create worn textures.

Hans makes the artwork look as realistic as possible. "Texture is all-important to create realism. The original model-makers made everything look battle-worn and well-used, so we do the same!"

INKING STAGE

The drawing is inked using a 0.18 mm Isograph pen. Hans mixes three drops of black ink with 15 drops of brown ink, making sure that the lines are not too dark.

The eraser is a vital artist's tool!

AT THE DESK

Jenssen's "desk" is his drawing board, cluttered with the tools he needs for each stage of the illustration process.

The penciling stage can take over 200 hours for complex artworks

PENCIL DRAWING

For the finished pencil drawing, Jenssen uses a 0.3 mm technical pencil with an HB lead which can be erased easily. The internal detail is often reworked, based on feedback from Lucasfilm or the author, or if Hans has a new idea.

WORKING IT OUT

Getting the angle and details of each illustration right is crucial. For the shuttle *Tydirium*, Jenssen spent hours watching the *Return of the Jedi* DVD to discern cockpit detail, annotating an early sketch (top left) with suggestions for crew stations. Thumbnail sketches (middle left) were sent to Lucasfilm and the author to discuss the best angle from which to draw the ship. For some vehicles a photograph or 3-D computer model would be used to obtain the correct angle. With the shuttle, Hans had no photos from the selected angle, so he had to use his drawing skills to get the correct perspective (bottom left).

FIRST VERSION

After the rough sketches are done, Hans draws an accurate view in pencil on layout paper. This version is simple but precise and shows where the cutaway areas will be.

INDEX

Bold page numbers refer to main entries.

DK PUBLISHING

EDITOR David Fentiman
ADDITIONAL EDITORIAL Alastair Dougall, Kathryn Hill and Lisa Stock
SENIOR DESIGNER Clive Savage
ADDITIONAL DESIGNERS Nick Avery, Mabel Chan,
Ian Ebstein, Mary Lytle and Toby Truphet
PRE-PRODUCTION PRODUCER Marc Staples
PRODUCER Kathleen McNally
INDEXER Hilary Bird
MANAGING EDITOR Sadie Smith
MANAGING ART EDITOR Ron Stobbart
CREATIVE MANAGER Sarah Harland
ART DIRECTOR Lisa Lanzarini
PUBLISHER Julie Ferris
PUBLISHING DIRECTOR Simon Beecroft

LUCASFILM LTD.

EXECUTIVE EDITOR Jonathan W. Rinzler
ART EDITOR Troy Alders
KEEPER OF THE HOLOCRON Leland Chee
DIRECTOR OF PUBLISHING Carol Roeder

ILLUSTRATOR ACKNOWLEDGEMENTS

Hans Jenssen would like to thank his good friend
Tom Evans for helping with designing Luke's
landspeeder, and his very tolerant family for
their support over the years. Also all the top
professionals whom he has been lucky enough
to work with at DK and Lucasfilm, especially his
brother in arms, Richard Chasemore.

Richard Chasemore would like to thank Lucasfilm
for their kind words, support and approval.
DK for believing in a young artist and still calling
with new projects! All the fans we meet at the
conventions that push us to greater heights of
detail. Of course my faithful dog Koco who sits with
me in my studio into the early hours, and my art
partner Hans Jenssen, Salute!

This edition published in 2015
First published in Great Britain in 2013 by
Dorling Kindersley Limited
80 Strand, London WC2R 0RL

001-187854-Aug/15

Material in this book was previously published in:
Star Wars: Complete Cross-Sections (2007), *Star Wars Revenge of the Sith: Incredible Cross-Sections* (2005),
Star Wars Attack of the Clones: Incredible Cross-Sections (2002), *Star Wars Episode I: Incredible Cross-Sections* (1999)
and *Star Wars: Incredible Cross-Sections* (1998)

Page design copyright © 2013, 2015 Dorling Kindersley Limited
A Penguin Random House Company

© & TM 2015 Lucasfilm Ltd.

All rights reserved. No part of this publication may be reproduced,
stored in a retrieval system, or transmitted in any form or by any means,
electronic, mechanical, photocopying, recording, or otherwise,
without the prior written permission of the copyright owner.

A CIP catalogue record for this book is available from the British Library.

ISBN: 978-0-2411-8032-7

Printed and bound in China

www.starwars.com
www.dk.com

A WORLD OF IDEAS:
SEE ALL THERE IS TO KNOW